THE CRY OF MERLIN:
JUNG, THE PROTOTYPICAL
ECOPSYCHOLOGIST

Also by Dennis Merritt

Jung and Ecopsychology
The Dairy Farmer's Guide to the Universe Volume I
ISBN 978-1-926715-42-1

Hermes, Ecopsychology, and Complexity Theory
The Dairy Farmer's Guide to the Universe Volume III
ISBN 978-1-926715-44-5

Land, Weather, Seasons, Insects: An Archetypal View
The Dairy Farmer's Guide to the Universe Volume IV
ISBN 978-1-926715-45-2

THE CRY OF MERLIN:
JUNG, THE PROTOTYPICAL
ECOPSYCHOLOGIST

THE DAIRY FARMER'S GUIDE
TO THE UNIVERSE VOLUME II

DENNIS L. MERRITT, PH.D.

The Cry of Merlin: Jung, the Prototypical Ecopsychologist
The Dairy Farmer's Guide to the Universe Volume 2
Copyright © 2012 by Dennis L. Merritt
First Edition
ISBN 978-1-926715-43-8 Paperback

Published simultaneously in Canada, the United Kingdom, and the United States of America by Fisher King Press. For information on obtaining permission for use of material from this work, submit a written request to: permissions@fisherkingpress.com

Fisher King Press
PO Box 222321
Carmel, CA 93922
www.fisherkingpress.com
info@fisherkingpress.com
+1-831-238-7799

Every effort has been made to trace all copyright holders; however, if any have been overlooked, the author will be pleased to make the necessary arrangements at the first opportunity. Many thanks to all who have directly and indirectly granted permission to quote their work, including:

From *C. G. Jung: His Myth in Our Time* by Marie-Louise von Franz, translated by William H. Kennedy, copyright 1975 by the C. G. Jung Foundation for Analytical Psychology, Inc., New York. Used by permission of Inner City Books.

From *Jung: His Life and Work*, 1991, by Barbara Hannah. Copyright 1976 by Barbara Hannah. Reprinted by permission of Chiron Publications.

From *Jung—A Biography* by Deirdre Bair, copyright 2003 by Little, Brown and Co. Reprinted by permission of Hachette Book Group USA.

From *Memories, Dreams, Reflections* by C. G. Jung, edited by Aniela Jaffe, translated by Richard and Clara Winston, translation copyright 1961, 1962, 1963 and renewed 1989,1990, 1991 by Random House, Inc. Used by permission of Pantheon Books, a division of Random House, Inc.

From *The Forsaken Garden: Four Conversations on the Deep Meaning of Environmental Illness* by Nancy Ryley, copyright 1998 by Quest Books. Used by permission of Quest Books.

CONTENTS

The four volumes of *The Dairy Farmer's Guide to the Universe* offer a comprehensive presentation of Jungian ecopsychology. Volume 1, *Jung and Ecopsychology*, examines the evolution of the Western dysfunctional relationship with the environment, explores the theoretical framework and concepts of Jungian ecopsychology, and describes how it could be applied to psychotherapy, our educational system, and our relationship with indigenous peoples. Volume 2, *The Cry of Merlin: Jung, the Prototypical Ecopsychologist*, reveals how an individual's biography can be treated in an ecopsychological manner and articulates how Jung's life experiences make him the prototypical ecopsychologist. Volume 3, *Hermes, Ecopsychology, and Complexity Theory*, provides an archetypal, mythological and symbolic foundation for Jungian ecopsychology. Volume 4, *Land, Weather, Seasons, Insects: An Archetypal View* describes how a deep, soulful connection can be made with these elements through a Jungian ecopsychological approach. This involves the use of science, myths, symbols, dreams, Native American spirituality, imaginal psychology and the *I Ching*. Together, these volumes provide what I hope will be a useful handbook for psychologists and environmentalists seeking to imagine and enact a healthier relationship with their psyches and the world of which they are a part.

My thanks to Craig Werner for his comprehensive and sensitive editorial work, and to Tom Lane and David McKee for their constructive comments.

To my father, my grandfathers, and The Grandfathers

xii

The peasant's alternating rhythm of work secures him unconscious satisfactions through its symbolical content—satisfactions which the factory workers and office employees do not know and can never enjoy. What do these know of his life with nature, of those grand moments when, as lord and fructifier of the earth, he drives his plough through the soil, and with a kingly gesture scatters the seed for the future harvest; of his rightful fear of the destructive power of the elements, of his joy in the fruitfulness of his wife who bears him the daughters and sons who mean increased working-power and prosperity?...From all this we city-dwellers, we modern machine-minders, are far removed.

—Carl Jung, CW 7, ¶ 428

INTRODUCTION

Carl Jung's life is one of the great psychological and spiritual journeys of the last century. As a biologist and ecologist I am impressed with how deeply Jung was connected with nature and how that connection affected the development of his ideas. His life provided the basis for his theoretical constructs, the practice of Jungian psychology, and the basic elements of Jungian ecopsychology presented in volume 1 of *The Dairy Farmer's Guide to the Universe*. Ecopsychology is a new field that emerged in the 1990s to examine how our values, perceptions and attitudes affect our relationship with the environment. Like deep ecology it explores ways of connecting us more deeply with the environment, calls for a deep analysis of our dysfunctional relationship with the environment, and examines the psychological dimensions of the challenges of developing a sustainable human culture.

Jung's holistic, integrated perspective on life and nature, shaped by and in turn shaping his concept of the archetypes, makes him a prototypical ecopsychologist and deep ecologist. Jung* viewed every psychology as a subjective confession and examining his life reveals both the profundity of and the lacuna in his constructs, particularly in relation to Christianity. (n 1) Delineating this lacuna and understanding Jung's ideas within the broader framework of his life, place and times can be seen as an ecopsychological exercise. Jung's identification with the archetypal figure of Merlin is associated with his interest in the Medieval attempt to address the questions of evil and the European pagan unconscious, which Jung considered to be the main questions of our time.

---

* Note: MDR refers throughout the text to C.G. Jung's *Memories, Dreams, Reflections* and CW refers throughout the text to *The Collected Works of C. G. Jung*.

CHAPTER 1

Jung's Formative Years and his Connection with Nature

Jung's deep connection with nature begins with his cultural and national experience of being Swiss. The Swiss are defined by their admiring relationship with their beautiful Alps. They are enthusiastic hikers, and the Alps are laced with breathtaking trails. One can hike for hours, turn a bend in the trail, and come across a small restaurant where a cup of hot chocolate can be had—nature and culture united. The Swiss national identity is based on the myth of the democratic, yeoman dairy farmers of the Alps—"alp" meaning "mountain meadow." They preserve this identity in stories like Wilhelm Tell and in subsidies for Alpine farmers—the higher the farm, the greater the subsidy. How else could a 21st century farmer survive by cutting hay with a scythe on a mountainside? The isolation of mountain valley villages kept alive a mythology of the land and its spirits long after other countries had banished these stories to academic presses and children's books. (n 2) To this day one can witness "pagan" festivals in many Swiss cities and towns. (n 3)

Jung was born into this archaic cultural and natural milieu in 1875 and spent his boyhood years in the country with Swiss peasants. As a psychologist he emphasized the importance of the natural and cultural background on an individual's nature. A significant cultural influence on Jung's development and character is the centuries-old democratic tradition in Switzerland. Barbara Hannah, a Jungian analyst who lived in Switzerland and wrote one of the best biographies on Jung, wrote, "Democracy, in the best sense of the word, is born and bred in the Swiss." (Hannah 1991, p. 12) Important government decisions are put to the direct vote of the people, who, like Jung, take their citizenship responsibilities seriously. Democracy at its best is an ecopsychological concept because all elements are given a voice and integrated into the whole. A second key factor was Switzerland's decision over 400 years ago to avoid external wars. Jung said the Swiss "introverted war" by using their warlike instincts against each other "in the form of domestic quarrels called 'political life.'" Although an improvement over projecting one's shadow (dark side) onto other nations, Jung believed "the only struggle that is really worth while [is] the fight against the overwhelming power-drive of the shadow." (CW 10, ¶ 455) Owning one's shadow is a humbling experience that inhibits the projection of evil onto others by way of justifying wars or decimating nature in the process of trying to control its unruly forces. Jung's Swiss heritage both aided and complicated his struggle with the shadow.

Born in a small village in rural Switzerland, Jung's experiences with the natural environment in his early years made a deep impact on his whole life. He was always close to nature in his youth and his contact with the peasants left him imbued as an adult with a certain realistic and down-to-earth attitude. (n 4) He was immersed in a Swiss landscape decades before the advent of automobiles and freeways, suburbs and TVs. His earliest memory was of lying in his baby stroller and noticing the soft play of sunlight on the leaves above him. (MDR, p. 6) He distinctly remembered seeing the Alps for the first time: an aunt held him up to see the sunset on Uetliberg in the distance, which became the land of his dreams. He was to spend his adult life living across from the Uetliberg in Zurich. As a child he remembered becoming completely enthralled by the dance of sunlight on the waves on the lake: his parents could not pull him away. "I must live near a lake, without water, I thought, nobody could live at all." (p. 7) As an adult he built a grand home on the lakeshore in Kusnacht just south of Zurich.

Jung was a lonely, isolated child who lived largely in his intrapsychic world as a consequence of his dysfunctional family situation and unusual childhood. His difficult early life added an archetypal dimension to his experience of nature. Powerful dreams, visions and spontaneous symbolic activities punctuated Jung's life and kept him connected with the archetypal realm. As a child he spent endless hours alone playing games he invented and only he could play. (Bair 2003, p. 22) He couldn't bear to be watched as he played. He made few friends and was described as being an "asocial monster." (p. 23) Jung grew up as an only child for the first 9-1/2 years of his life, the son of a poor country minister in a society where class and money were important. Both parents were from a long line of ministers and Jung had many uncles who were ministers. He suffered from the minister's child syndrome where parishioners watch the family with a critical eye, taking a secret delight in their missteps and problems. (Hannah 1991, p. 27) Not surprisingly, spiritual questions became an early focus in his life.

Jung's mother was severely depressed when Jung was born and for years after spent much time alone in her room. She found rural life away from family roots in Basel to be dismal and suffered through several miscarriages before Jung was born. Her marriage did not go well, and Jung overheard terrible fights as his father's seething anger exploded at his mother behind closed doors. (Bair 2003, p. 20) Jung suffered from a terrible eczema he later attributed to being around his dismal parents. Attachment theorists understand the trauma to Jung's psyche when his mother disappeared into the hospital for months at a time when Jung was 3 years old. He felt abandoned by his mother and for decades distrusted love and women. (MDR, p. 8) (see Appendix G: Jung's Eros Wound and his Image of God)

A maid who cared for Jung while his mother was away came to symbolize the "essence of womanhood" and later the basis of his concept of the anima, the "inner woman" in a man. She seemed "very strange and yet strangely familiar." Jung felt she belonged only to him and was somehow connected "with other mysterious things I could not understand." (MDR, p. 8) The situation was compounded by a histrionic mother who openly and enthusiastically talked about ghosts and spirits that visited her at night. Jung was terrified of his mother at night and once had an apparition of a ghost with detaching heads emerging from her bedroom. (p. 18) He often had choking fits and once nearly fell into the Rhine River, an incident he later attributed to "a fatal resistance to life in this world." (p. 9)

Adding to this background were three powerful experiences that provided the context for a nightmare at age 3 or 4 that laid the psychological foundation for the rest of Jung's life and a sense of a spirit of the earth. The first was watching his father preside over the funerals of people who drowned in the Rhine. Jung was fascinated by these victims who got buried in black boxes in the ground, rendering them no longer present after Lord Jesus had taken them to himself. (MDR, p. 10) The second experience was playing beside the road in front of his house and a Catholic priest came walking by. Jung fled in a panic at the sight of this unusual man wearing a dress. He had overheard his father speaking in anxious tones about the Jesuits, so they must be dangerous people. (p. 10, 11) (n 5) The third ingredient for the nightmare was a childhood misunderstanding of a bedtime song his mother sang to him. It seemed to young Jung she was singing about Jesus as some kind of winged bird who reluctantly "took" children like bitter medicine to prevent Satan from eating them. (p. 9, 10)

In Jung's nightmare, he discovered an underground temple hewn out of stone that enclosed a giant phallus sitting on a golden throne. A single eye atop its head gazed upward into an aura of brightness. Jung was terrified that the motionless object might start creeping towards him. His mother's voice called out, "That is the man-eater!" (MDR, p. 11, 12) Jung awoke in terror and was afraid to fall asleep for several nights afterwards.

The dream haunted him for years. Decades later he realized the phallus had a sanctity that was worshipped in ancient rituals and ceremonies. (n 6) He interpreted the underground temple to be a tomb, and linked the phallus as the source of the light above it with the etymology of the word phallus: "shining, bright." (MDR, p. 12, 13) (n 7) Jesus was never quite acceptable or lovable after the nightmare because of his association with death and "his underground counterpart." The dream "brought the Above and the Below together" while the phallus as an underground God "not to be named" initiated Jung "into the secrets of the earth" and "the realm of darkness." The dream set his life's goal: "to bring the greatest possible amount of light" into that realm. (p. 15) This "ur-experience," as Jung described it, became the foundation of his concept of the Spirit in nature and of God in matter, and eventually led to his psycho-spiritual interest in alchemy. The dream encapsulated a basic element in Jung's personality and his relationship to his inner and outer worlds as a veiled, secret and hidden phallic energy "undisclosed apart from its maternal or feminine containment." (Noel 1974, p. 239, 240) (see Appendix H: Jung's Phallic Self Image)

Jung confessed at the end of his life that his childhood experiences of processes in the background shaped his entire life and his early dreams "determined my course from the beginning." (MDR, p. 356) (n 8) He said his nightmare ushered in the unconscious beginnings of his intellectual life. (p. 15) An experience that powerful and frightening can stimulate the mind of a child to be more vigilant and struggle to figure things out, a development that can produce a premature split between psyche and soma. (Winnicott 1949/1975)

There are symbolic, mythic and sacred dimensions of the phallus associated with intellectual life, a *joie de vivre*, Eros and healing—all strong qualities in Jung's adult life. (n 9) The sacred dimension of the phallus is particularly important for the Western male since Christianity has no sacred image of phallic energy. The sharpest contrast is presented in a Hindu myth of Super Shiva—Creator, Maintainer, and Destroyer—worshipped as a prodigious phallus. (n 10)

Jung survived his childhood aided by symbolic activities in nature. He was fascinated with fire and stone between the ages of 7 and 9 and tried to keep a fire burning forever in the small cave of an old stone wall, a "living" fire that had "an unmistakable aura of sanctity." (MDR, p. 19, 20) He loved to sit on "his stone" that he felt a secret relationship with. It perplexed him for hours at a time whether he was the one sitting on the stone or was he the stone upon which young Jung sat. He could so completely identify with the stone that he had the unpleasant feeling of being out of himself. Such experiences lent a "quality of eternity" to his childhood—the eternal, archetypal domain that every child experiences. (p. 20, 21) (n 11)

Jung engaged in a highly symbolic activity at age 10 that helped transform the fearful phallic energy of his nightmare into a more human and personal form. (Hannah 1991, p. 34) He carved an old ruler into a manikin and painted it black. The figure had several associations to the men who stood around the graves at funerals: it had a frock coat, top hat, and boots. He lay the manikin in a little bed in a pencil case that included *his* stone—a smooth stone from the Rhein that Jung painted so it looked like it had an upper and lower half. He hid the pencil case in the attic where no one could find it. Occasionally a little scroll of paper was placed in it upon which Jung had written, in a secret language, the things that pleased him; a communication that "had the character of a solemn ceremonial act." "It was an inviolable secret which must never be betrayed for the safety of my life depended on it," Jung wrote. (MDR, p. 21, 22) He would think about the manikin whenever he felt guilty, hurt, or oppressed by his father's irritability or his mother's invalidism. (Jung had many anxiety dreams and choking fits prior to puberty associated with the unbearable atmosphere at home.) (p. 18) The manikin exemplified what he called a symbol: "The best unconscious expression at the time for something that is essentially unknown." (Hannah 1991, p. 33)

He subsequently forgot about the manikin until age 35 when he read about soul stones (stones believed to carry the souls of people) during preliminary studies for *Symbols of Transformation*. Such stones are found near Arlesheim, France and were the revered *churingas* of the Australian aborigines. Stones are considered to be eternal because it appears they will last forever. The stone was the supply of the life force for Jung's manikin—a very pagan notion. (n 12) In the Von Eschenbach version of the Grail story the grail is a stone. Jung's readings about soul stones gave him his first awareness of what he would come to call archetypes—

psychic components of our collective unconscious. The adult Jung recognized the manikin as "a little cloaked god of the ancient world, a Telesphoros such as stands on the monuments of Asklepios [Greek god of healing] and reads to him from a scroll." (MDR, p. 23) (see Appendix H) Antique gods "sometimes represented by a human figure and sometimes by a phallus," were placed in special receptacles for sacred objects (kistas). (Hannah 1991, p. 34)

Jung attributed his childhood nightmare to more than dysfunctional family dynamics and experiencing a fearful side of his mother. At its core Jung believed he had imbibed a "religious faith [that] had lost its original living quality" and had been reduced to empty religious forms and rigid collective values. (von Franz 1975, p. 15) When God seems to die, the energy formally contained by the cultural God image turns dark and negative as it returns to the underworld, the depths of the collective unconscious. It energizes the depths and can first appear there in the form of a phallus. (p. 16, 17, 29, 30) Christ's energies become "God's reflection in physical nature." (CW 13, ¶ 284; von Franz 1975, p. 30) In the depths, the energies can be transformed "into a hidden nature-god of creativity," transformed into positive, life-enforcing and supportive energies as illustrated by Jung's manikin with its stone. (von Franz 1975, p. 29) (n 13)

Jung considered the secrets of the manikin, the phallus dream, and the Jesuit experience to be the essential features of his boyhood, belonging to a mysterious realm associated with nature. (MDR, p. 22) Late in life he would extol the virtues of having an inviolable secret to further the development of one's unique character and an inner guidance. (n 14) He felt it was vitally important for a person to "sense that he lives in a world which in some respects is mysterious," where inexplicable things happen that can't be anticipated. (MDR, p. 356)

Nature reflected Jung's inner state as a child; it incorporated both the beauty of the bright daylight world and a world of shadows "filled with frightening, unanswerable questions which had me at their mercy." (MDR, p. 19) His interest "in plants, animals, and stones grew" as he searched nature for answers to the strange mystery of life. His Christian beliefs were qualified by "that thing under the ground," a secret "that people don't know about." (p. 22)

When attending Gymnasium in Basel during his twelfth year, Jung began a neurotic pattern of fainting spells that kept him out of school for 6 months. (n 15) During that time he plunged into the "world of the mysterious" that entailed avid reading in his father's library and spending a great deal of time in nature. (MDR, p. 30, 31) Everything in nature "seemed alive and indescribably marvelous" as he tried to crawl "into the very essence of nature and away from the whole human world." (p. 32) Many children keep some semblance of sanity in difficult childhoods by escaping into nature if only by climbing a favorite tree in their backyard. Eventually Jung was embarrassed to realize he had led himself astray by "my passion for being alone, my delight in solitude." He forced himself to recover, an event he saw as marking the beginnings of a life of conscientiousness and "an unusual diligence." (p. 32)

The experience with the manikin and the heroic ego-strengthening effort of overcoming the fainting spells helped Jung emerge from the "dense cloud" of his childhood in his eleventh or twelfth year. (Hannah 1991, p. 44) What emerged was an individual with a firm sense of authority and self-will. Previously *he had been* willed to do things. (MDR, p. 32, 33) What also emerged was a dissociative experience of living in two ages simultaneously and being two different people. One person was a paltry ego now aware of his poor background and the other was an old man of dignity, power, authority, respect and awe; a man of the eighteenth century, a century with which Jung felt a curious and strong identity. (p. 33, 34) The manikin had evolved into a formulation of the Self that could serve as the archetypal base for the development of a healthy and whole ego. The "old man" compensated for Jung's inadequacies in dealing with a harsh world and it kept him in touch with a childlike sense of wholeness and the archetypal realm of the collective unconscious in all of us.

In addition, Jung started praying to God, a unique being of a secret nature for whom "it was impossible to form any correct conception." God was not linked with Jung's distrust of his familiar image of Jesus or associated with black robed priests. (MDR, p. 27) His complex apprehension of God and nature would continue to occupy his thoughts as he passed through adolescence.

CHAPTER 2

The Dark Side of God and "God's World" as Nature

The dualities Jung felt in his life, nature, and God were crystallized in "the most shattering" experience in his life—an experience at age twelve of "the dark side of God." (Bair 2003, p. 846 note 41) It began with Jung walking by the Basel Cathedral on a fine summer day and being overwhelmed by its beauty and the beauty of the world. As he thought of God the creator high above on a golden throne, he suddenly choked up and was numbed by the feeling there was something he dare not think. After struggling valiantly for three days and nights to prevent the forbidden thought from breaking through, he finally arrived at the conclusion God himself was forcing him to think this thought. He felt he was leaping into hell fire as he let the image emerge: God high in heaven let loose a gigantic turd from beneath his golden throne that destroyed the Basel Cathedral! (MDR, p. 36-39)

Jung immediately felt an enormous, indescribable relief and a sense of grace, unutterable bliss, and illumination. He felt freed by the realization that "the immediate living God...stands, omnipotent and free, above His Bible and His Church, who calls upon man to partake of His freedom, and can force him to renounce his own views and convictions in order to fulfill without reserve the command of God...One must be utterly abandoned to God; nothing matters but fulfilling His will." (MDR, p. 40) (n 16) He was shamed by this horrible, secret realization that God could be something terrible, but also felt a kind of distinction for knowing this. (p. 40, 41) (n 17)

This powerful experience of God's dark side increased Jung's sense of a great mystery in life and in nature and laid the foundation for his reliance upon messages from the unconscious. He felt liberated and began a life-long and private task of intensely searching God's intentions. It emboldened him to pursue thoughts and philosophical and spiritual paths beyond the pale of conventional viewpoints.

Finding no readings in his father's library to support his experience, Jung was left to brood over his dark secret. At such times he felt strangely reassured and calmed when he sat on his stone. The conflict would cease when he thought he was the stone—the Other that was timeless and imperishable. While Jung felt he was the sum of his emotions, the stone was eternal, with no uncertainties and no need to communicate. (MDR, p. 42)

At age 15 Jung still suffered many rejections and felt "unworthy, undeserving and unlikable." (Bair 2003, p. 30) While compensating for insecurity and guilt over his many faults, he began to grow more aware of having two personalities. Personality No. 1 was his faulty ego, while Personality No. 2 was closely associated with God *in* nature. It had evolved out of his experience of the timeless world of stone and the phallus-manikin-18th century man:

> [No. 2 was old], skeptical, mistrustful, remote from the world of men, but close to nature, the earth, the sun, the moon, the weather, all living creatures, and above all close to the night, to dreams, and to whatever "God" worked directly in him. (MDR, p. 44, 45)

Nature seemed to be a better expression of God than His human creation. To enter God's realm was like entering a temple where one was

> transformed and suddenly overpowered by a vision of the whole cosmos, so that he could only marvel and admire, forgetful of himself. Here lived the "Other," who knew God as a hidden, personal, and at the same time suprapersonal secret. Here nothing separated man from God; indeed, it was as though the human mind looked down upon Creation simultaneously with God. (MDR, p. 45)

Noticeable by its absence is the archetype of Eros in the form of love, intimacy and the warmth of human relationships, of the archetypal image of Jesus as a god of love. Jung experienced a feeling of self-worth and being his true self when he passed into "the peace and solitude of this 'Other,' Personality No. 2." (p. 45) At age 14 he felt God was physically present when he was atop Rigi mountain on Lake Lucern; *that* was His world, "the real world, the secret." (p. 78)

During that fourteenth year he had a Dionysian experience of "an entirely new and unexpected state of consciousness" when he got "shamefully, gloriously, triumphantly drunk." The painful dichotomies of inner/outer, I/other dissolved into a oneness with the universe and everything in it—"a premonition of beauty and meaning." (MDR, p. 77) Dionysus was the Greek god of the vine, wine making, ritual madness, and ecstasy. His energies are associated with the goddess cults of the ancient Middle East where beer and wine were made in the temples for the wild, erotic festivals of the Sacred Prostitute. Ecstatic and erotic energies were used to enter divine and prophetic states. (see volume 3 of *The Dairy Farmer's Guide*, Appendix G: The Sacred Prostitute and the Erotic Feminine and Appendix H: The Black Goddess)

Church gradually became a torment for the adolescent Jung because men dared to pretend they knew God's will and intentions. Jung was devastated by his first communion at age 15 when he felt God was absent. (MDR, p. 52-56) People knew "nothing of the vast despair, the overpowering elation and the outpouring of grace which...constituted the essence of God." (p. 55) Jung had a growing sense of destiny and responsibility for the fate assigned to him. "I knew that I had to find the answer out of my deepest self," he wrote, "that I was alone before God, and that God alone asked me these terrible things." (p. 47) Often he had "the feeling that in all decisive matters I was no longer among men, but was alone with God." Then he was outside time and "belonged to the centuries...Talks with the 'Other' were my profoundest experiences:...a bloody struggle...[and a] supreme ecstasy." (p. 48)

There was no one he could communicate these thoughts to. He realized the dark side of human nature, above all in himself. (Hannah 1991, p. 50) Jung played alone and spent much time alone in his secret world, sustained by his connection with nature. This long and profound passage reflects his adolescent feelings about animals, plants, and stones and their relationship to God's world:

> Because they are so closely akin to us and share our unknowingness, I loved all warm-blooded animals who have souls like ourselves and with whom, so I thought, we have an instinctive understanding. We experience joy and sorrow, love and hate, hunger and thirst, fear and trust in common—all the essential features of existence with the exception of speech, sharpened consciousness, and science. And although I admired science in the conventional way, I also saw it giving rise to alienation and aberration from God's world, as leading to a degeneration which animals were not capable of. Animals were dear and faithful, unchanging and trustworthy. People I now distrusted more than ever.

Insects I did not regard as proper animals, and I took cold-blooded vertebrates to be a rather lowly intermediate stage on the way down to the insects. Creatures in this category were objects for observation and collection, curiosities merely, alien and extra-human; they were manifestations of impersonal life and more akin to plants than to human beings.

The earthly manifestations of "God's world" began with the realm of plants, as a kind of direct communication from it. It was as though one were peering over the shoulder of the Creator, who, thinking Himself unobserved, was making toys and decorations. Man and the proper animals, on the other hand, were bits of God that had become independent. That was why they could move about on their own and choose their abodes. Plants were bound for good or ill to their places. They expressed not only the beauty but also the thoughts of God's world, with no intent of their own and without deviation. Trees in particular were mysterious and seemed to me direct embodiments of the incomprehensible meaning of life. For that reason the woods were the place where I felt closest to its deepest meaning and to its awe-inspiring workings.

This impression was reinforced when I became acquainted with Gothic cathedrals. But there the infinity of the cosmos, the chaos of meaning and meaninglessness, of impersonal purpose and mechanical law, were wrapped in stone. This contained and at the same time was the bottomless mystery of being, the embodiment of spirit. What I dimly felt to be my kinship with stone was the divine nature in both, in the dead and the living matter. (MDR, p. 67, 68)

Jung attained a sense of security and a solid grounding when he realized his mother's No. 2 personality was connected to nature like his No. 2. He didn't realize at the time how "pagan" this was, contrasting "most strangely with her Christian surface and her conventional assertions of faith." (MDR, p. 90, 91) His mother's mental health had improved to the degree that she felt warm and amicable on the surface, but she had a powerful, authoritative side in her No. 2 personality. No. 2 occurred unexpectedly and in a fearful manner. (p. 48-50) His mother seemed uncanny at night, "like one of those seers who is at the same time a strange animal, like a priestess in a bear's cave." In those moments she embodied what Jung called the "natural mind," "the 'mind' which says absolutely straight and ruthless things...It wells up from the earth like a natural spring, and brings with it a peculiar wisdom of nature." (p. 50 note 3)

Jung extended a child-like imagination and playfulness into late adolescence. At age 15 or 16 he had a long, systematic fantasy that lasted for several months. He imagined living alone with a great library in a well-fortified medieval castle tower, the imaginary forerunner of his retreat tower he built at Bollingen as an adult. The imaginary tower housed an inverted copper tree whose rootlets extracted "a kind of spiritual essence" from the air, which was mysteriously converted into gold coins in the basement—an alchemical motif. This fantasy was followed by two years of using mud and stones to build castles and fortified emplacements. (MDR, p. 80-82)

Contrary to the Christian dogma Jung was reading at age 16, he believed there could be no human relationship to God because God was too unknown. In God is everything, therefore he couldn't have a distinguishable character, which would be subjective and limited. (MDR, p. 56, 57) Jung read nothing about God's dark side—"His vindictiveness, His dangerous wrathfulness, His incomprehensible conduct" nor did he read of a creation that is "immeasurably beautiful...[and] quite as horrible." (p. 58) Jung briefly considered theology as a profession a few years later until he realized theologians knew nothing of religious experience. Rather, they engaged in discussions of "doctrinal opinions" while living "in a world of social and intellectual certitudes." (p. 73, 74)

CHAPTER 3

Faust, Kant, Science and Nietzsche

Jung's mother, speaking through Personality No. 2, suggested he read *Faust* which Jung said "poured into my soul like a miraculous balm." Jung realized the Devil was more important than Faust because he could "frustrate God's plan to make a perfect world," and revealed "the mysterious role [evil] played in delivering man from darkness and suffering." Personality No. 2 felt fully addressed by Goethe's *Faust* because it recognized the existence, vitality and redemptive qualities of the dark forces and was somehow related to "the mystery of the Mothers"—the world of nature. (MDR, p. 60) Jung read over a vast range of topics over the next several years to distract him from Personality No. 2. Increasingly No. 2 led to depressions because Jung could find no answers to his questions. Philosophers did not have Jung's sense that "God was...one of the most certain and immediate of experiences." (p. 62)

When grief and rage threatened to overwhelm him, he would slip into his No. 2 personality. That put everything into a timeless, objective perspective:

> It was as though a breath of the great world of stars and endless space had touched me, or as if a spirit had invisibly entered the room—the spirit of one who had long been dead and yet was perpetually present in timelessness until far into the future. (MDR, p. 66)

> To "God's world" belonged everything superhuman— dazzling light, the darkness of the abyss, the cold impassivity of infinite space and time, and the uncanny grotesqueness of the irrational world of chance. (p. 72)

His depressive states improved between his sixteenth and nineteenth years as Personality No. 1 emerged more distinctly as life in a city school occupied more of his time. Knowledge increasingly permeated the world of his intuitive premonitions. Readings in philosophy showed that many of his intuitions had historical analogues. He felt a "breath of life" in Meister Eckhart (MDR, p. 68, 69), and responded strongly to Schopenhauer's understanding of the evil, confusion, and suffering in the world and the cruelty in nature. Schopenhauer said creation had a fundamental flaw attributable to "the blindness of the world-creating Will." (p. 69) Kant became Jung's favorite philosopher, helping him realize that everything comes out of the psyche; there is no Archimedean standpoint from which we can stand outside the psyche and form objective opinions. (n 18)

Jung's philosophical development extended from his seventeenth year until well into medical studies when he underwent a "revolution-ary" change. (MDR, p. 70) He showed great interest in many things, became noticeably more accessible and communicative, and made friends. But his courage to speak openly of his ideas generated suspi-cions and rejection in others who didn't know what he was talking about. He learned not to speak about Kant, Schopenhauer, or paleontol-ogy which were esoteric matters that belonged to the realm of "God's world." (p. 71, 72)

Personality No. 1 was also strengthened around age 16 as his interest in science grew. "Anyone could have fantasies, but real knowledge was another matter." (MDR, p. 82) Scientific knowledge formed a part of God's world and "filled the great canvas with vivid colors and figures." (p. 75)

Jung had many vehement discussions with his father in his later teens. (n 19) He believed his father's main problem was a spiritual crisis and blamed the church for the alienation between them. The church trapped his father in a spiritless existence Jung thought, then offered him no way out. Theologians had never seen "the light that shineth in the darkness," so one had to believe without hope. (MDR, p. 93) "The arch sin of faith...was that it forestalled experience." (p. 94) In an interview late in life, Jung said he didn't believe in God, rather, he "knew." He couldn't believe in anything; he had to have a reason to think something was true or not (Jung 1977, p. 427, 428, 437), basing this statement on a series of inner experiences of God going back to his childhood nightmare.

Looking back, Jung realized how much his development as a child anticipated his father's and the West's religious collapse which had been centuries in the making. "Although we human beings have our own personal life, we are yet in large measure the representatives, the victims and promoters of a collective spirit whose years are counted in centuries...Thus at least a part of our being lives in the centuries." (MDR, p. 91) This was Jung's Personality No. 2 that he later named the collective unconscious, associating its cultural dimension with our dysfunctional relationship with nature.

Jung entered Basel University a semester before his father died at age 54. University was good for him. Everything was intellectually alive; he made friends, and discussed and lectured with great confidence in his fraternity on philosophical, psychological, and theological subjects. Religious theory was one of his main interests. To counter the materialism rampant in the university environment at that time "Jung argued for the reinstatement of 'the mystery of a metaphysical world, a metaphysical order' to the center of the Christian religion." (Bair 2003, p. 46)

He wanted most to study archaeology, especially Egyptian and Babylonian antiquity, but abruptly decided to study science because of dreams that "removed all doubts" about his academic direction. In one dream he discovered a wonderful, giant, three-foot radiolarian in a hidden, circular pool in a woods. A radiolarian is a type of one-celled animal that lives in water and has intricate patterns on its hard surfaces. It was "the strangest and most wonderful creature: a round animal, shimmering in opalescent hues, and consisting of innumerable little cells, or of organs shaped like tentacles...It aroused in me an intense desire for knowledge." (MDR, p. 85) As a numinous living sphere in a circular pool, it was an image of the Self, a God image appearing in nature. Being hidden in the deep woods indicates its distance from man's conscious world. (von Franz 1975, p. 31)

Jung was fascinated when he read Nietzsche during his University years and disturbed that Nietzsche had lost all contact with reality and went insane. Jung's reaction to Nietzsche helped deepen the interest in science that supported Personality No. 1. He realized the connection between his Personality No. 2 and Nietzsche's *Zarathustra*. (MDR, p. 102). He felt that Nietzsche made the grave mistake of speaking openly about "the thing not to be named"—the No. 2 realm whose existence the world had no knowledge of, which frightens people and precipitates a negative reaction. (p. 103)

Interest in science and zoology led Jung to study medicine which was less expensive than training for a purely scientific career. The empiricism of science satisfied the needs of his No. 1 personality; the need of No. 2 for meaning and spirituality was met by the humanities and historical studies, including comparative religion which was related to philosophy:

> No. 2 had no definable character at all;...born, living, dead, everything in one; a vision of life. Though pitilessly clear about himself, he was unable to express himself through the dense, dark medium of No. 1, though he longed to do so....No. 1 regarded No. 2 as a region of inner darkness... Light reigned [in No. 2]...Here were meaning and historical continuity, in strong contrast to the incoherent fortuitous- ness of No. 1's life, *which had no real points of contact with its environment.* (emphasis added) (MDR, p. 87)

Jung felt an inner security and sense of belonging to humanity because *Faust*—Goethe's "answer...to his times"—personified No. 2 and was in secret accord with the Middle Ages. (p. 87)

The difficulties Jung was experiencing between the two personalities reflect the difficulties of relating to the enticing powers of the arche- typal realm. From the perspective of No. 2, God does and does not want to become conscious, does and does not want to be made known by manifesting in time and space and being subject to its restrictions.

A dream at this time made Jung aware of the dangers of identifying with Personality No. 2. He dreamt he was trying to keep a little candle lit in the cup of his hand as he moved forward into a fierce night wind. He saw a gigantic and terrifying black figure following him. Upon waking Jung realized the shadow in the foggy mist was actually brought into being by the light reflecting off of it. No. 1 was the bearer of the light, the little light of consciousness: "My own understanding is the sole treasure I possess, and the greatest. Though infinitely small and fragile in comparison with the powers of darkness, it is still a light, my only light." (MDR, p. 87, 88) Jung interpreted the dream to mean he was to go forward into the world in the role of No. 1, "into study, moneymak- ing, responsibilities, entanglements, confusions, errors, submissions, defeats": the limitations of the present and three-dimensionality. While alive, one had to exert a mighty effort to find a satisfactory answer that would push against the great storm of time—the dark and power- ful forces of the collective unconscious associated with the ancestors. These were the cultural forces and problems left unsolved by previous generations. "Adam must once have left Paradise in this manner; Eden had become a specter for him, and light was where a stony field had to be tilled in the sweat of his brow." (p. 88) Jung now realized that in the light of consciousness, the inner realm of light appears as a gigantic shadow. He finally understood why people seemed embarrassed and estranged from him whenever he alluded to this inner realm. (p. 89) Throughout his university years and through the first nine years of his professional career at Burgholzli Hospital, Jung would go into the world almost exclusively in his No. 1 personality. (Hannah 1991, p. 95) No. 1 was "merely a part of the far more comprehensive No. 2" which now acquired an autonomous personality, a spirit of timeless, historical character. (MDR, p. 89, 90) Although he had to leave No. 2 behind, he could in no way deny or invalidate it because it had superior intelligence necessary for the creation of dreams and was "a spirit who could hold his own against the world of darkness." (p. 89)

Jung would come to renounce any identification with Personality No. 2. He chose to describe the inner world in an objective, detached manner, developing an I-Thou position in relating to it as an autonomous phenomenon. Ego inflation is prevented by critical conscious discrimination and renouncing claims to spiritual power. The ego, as the center of consciousness, can be seen as "a relatively constant personification of the unconscious" that allows the unconscious to become aware of itself (CW 14, ¶ 129)—it allows God to become conscious.

Another important development coming out of Jung's adolescence was the deep interest he developed in spiritualism broadly related to his sense of a spirit in nature. It began with regular participation in the séances of a 15 year old cousin on his mother's side. He studied the contents of the communications his cousin received and later wrote his doctoral thesis on his observations, "On the Psychology and Pathology of So-Called Occult Phenomena." Through visions and the spirits who spoke through his cousin, Jung learned "how a No. 2 personality is formed, how it enters into a child's consciousness and finally integrates it into itself." (MDR, p. 107) In Jung's thesis, Anthony Stevens detects "the origins of two ideas which were to become central to the practice of analytical psychology: (1) that part-personalities or 'complexes' existing in the unconscious psyche can 'personate' in trances, dreams, and hallucinations, and (2) that the real work of personality development proceeds at the unconscious level." (Stevens 1994, p. 9, 10 quoted in Bair 2003, p. 672 note 34)

Jung read virtually the entire literature on spiritualism available at the time. It gave him his first sense of the objective dimension of the psyche (the collective unconscious) because "it could be established that at all times and all over the world the same stories had been reported again and again." (MDR, p. 99) He believed occult phenomena "should...be explored and discussed in a scientific spirit." (Hannah 1991, p. 66) Jung had a strong rational side, but "always felt under an obligation to do all he could to understand, or at least to accept, the inexplicable." (p. 67)

Jung was astonished when even his closest friends reacted with derision, disbelief or anxious defensiveness to spiritualist phenomena. Although he couldn't attest to the absolute certainty of things like ghosts and table turnings, Jung said he

> found such possibilities extremely interesting and attractive. They added another dimension to my life; the world gained depth and background...

> After all, there was nothing preposterous or world-shaking in the idea that there might be events which overstepped the limited categories of space, time and causality...Plainly the urban world knew nothing about the country world, the real world of mountains, woods, and rivers, of animals and "God's thoughts" (plants and crystals)...It bolstered my self-esteem, for I realized that for all its wealth of learning the urban world was mentally rather limited. (MDR, p. 99, 100)

CHAPTER 4

The World of Psychiatry and Sigmund Freud

Jung was on the verge of becoming a medical researcher upon comple-
tion of medical school when a psychiatry book changed his life's direction. Krafft-Ebing's textbook, which Jung studied for his medical exams,
described psychiatry as entailing more than describing symptoms for
classifying mental illnesses, which was how psychiatry was practiced in
the late 1800s. Krafft-Ebing viewed psychiatry as a subjective engagement between doctor and patient where the doctor tried to achieve
some objectivity based on personal life experience. With the "whole
of his own personality" the doctor relates to the patient. People were
to be regarded as whole beings that included pathological variations,
with illness being a "disease of the personality." (MDR, p. 109) Jung
was ecstatic when he realized psychiatry satisfied both of his personalities; scientific and objective nature was on a par with the personal and
subjective.

His friends thought he was crazy to give up a sensible career in medical research to pursue such an obscure profession, but after his exams in
1900 he took up a post as a low-level assistant in the famous Burgholzli
Mental Hospital in Zurich. Its highly regarded chief, Eugene Bleuler,
insisted the staff live among the patients and establish a rapport with
them. (Bair 2003, p. 56, 57) Jung benefited from the broad and deep
experience of working in the state hospital with severely disturbed
people from across social and economic spectrums. He was particularly
good with schizophrenics, wrote his first book about them, and realized their tragic life stories within the psychotic fantasies. By working with the psyche *in extremis* "we encounter the substratum of our
own natures." (MDR, p. 127) Jung changed his focus to the study of
mythology in 1909 when he realized that he could not treat psychosis
unless he understood symbolism; the inner experience of the mentally
ill often reaches mythic dimensions. There was no difference between

unconscious symbolism in the sane or insane; the difference is that it overwhelms the psychotic. (Hannah 1991, p. 84)

Jung credited Freud for introducing psychology to psychiatry, by attempting to understand individual cases and not just categorizing and studying the types of mental illness. (MDR, p. 114, 168) Clinical diagnoses give the doctor a certain orientation, but the therapist must be able to understand an individual's suffering and life story in order to be effective. (p. 124) "The problem is always the whole person, never the symptom alone" (p. 117)—a perspective reflecting an ecology of the psyche, an interactive Gestalt of energies.

A pioneer psychotherapist, Jung began to develop his therapeutic approach at Burgholzli. He was deliberately unsystematic and guarded against theoretical assumptions because "the cure ought to grow naturally out of the patient himself. Psychotherapy and analysis are as varied as are human individuals." (MDR, p. 131) In a thoroughgoing analysis, the doctor becomes an integral part of the patient's dilemma and the doctor's whole being is challenged as he is himself transformed in the process. This is a Hermetic approach where there is no chasm between "authority" and patient—they share an ecology of the psyche. It is important for the therapist to have a personal experience of the numinosity of the archetypes or they will tend to over- or underestimate it in their practice. (p. 144) The therapist must understand herself first and know how to cope with her own problems because the therapist herself is the instrument. Therapists must also pay attention to how their unconscious is responding to the patient; dreams are helpful in this regard.

Jung believed many modern neurotics would not have been divided against themselves if they had lived in times past: "If they had lived in a period and in a milieu in which man was still linked by myth with the world of the ancestors, *and thus with nature truly experienced and not merely seen from outside*, they would have been spared this division with themselves." (emphasis added) (MDR, p. 144)

Jung found the "so-called intellectuals" to be "the most difficult as well as the most ungrateful patients, apart from habitual liars." They use "compartment psychology" to separate intellect from feeling: this forecloses any resolution of a neurosis. (MDR, p. 144, 145)

Jung married Emma Rauschenbach in 1903, the second richest heiress in Switzerland (n 20), and became a popular lecturer at the University of Zurich beginning in 1905. His private practice grew as he gained international recognition with his excellent research on the word association experiment, which demonstrated the existence of unconscious processes. Jung called these processes "complexes"—emotionally charged contents that interfered with conscious intent, such as fulfilling the researcher's request to make quick associations to prescribed words. The similarity between the activity of complexes and Freud's theory of repression could not be ignored. Jung began a personal and professional relationship with Freud after meeting him in Vienna for the first time in 1907. They talked without pause for 13 hours. "A world happened then," Jung said. (Bair 2003, p. 117) "In my experience up to that time, no one else could compare with him...I found him extremely intelligent, shrewd and altogether remarkable." (MDR, p. 149) (n 21)

Jung was 31, professionally established, and already developing important psychological concepts when he met Freud. Nineteen years Jung's senior, Freud was recognized by both to be a father figure for Jung. Jung was eager to learn what he could from Freud's genius, but had reservations from the start. Freud, at first ready to pass the mantle of psychoanalysis on to Jung, was dogmatic about his positions, particularly his theory of sexuality. He saw psychoanalysis as being *his* field with himself as the ultimate authority. (n 22)

Jung soon realized that sexuality had become Freud's religion, a numinosum, as revealed by Freud's unduly emotional and irrational tone when speaking of it. Jung believed Freud was deceiving himself by thinking he was being scientific, objective, and beyond religious taint. The jealous God Freud lost was now sought below in the unconscious in a role as *deus abscondus*—a hidden or concealed god. Only the name had changed—the substitute god "was no less insistent, exacting, domineering, threatening, and morally ambivalent than the original one... [with] not one wit the less of urgency, anxiety, compulsiveness, etc." (MDR, p. 151, 152) Freud was distorting the human psyche by forcing it into the Procrustean bed of his sexual theory, a theory that art and culture were "a mere farce, the morbid consequence of repressed sexuality." (p. 149, 150) Jung thought Freud was a bitter man, "his own worst enemy," because his rational, scientific, Enlightenment perspective precluded acknowledging sexuality as a numinosum, an inner daimon. Freud saw sexuality in an exclusively biological manner, using a concretistic terminology that denied its spiritual significance. (p. 152)

Jung also criticized Freud for ignoring the historical dimensions of human existence—archetypal influences extending over millennia of time which profoundly affect our worldviews. Examples are the

Judeo-Christian perspectives on the feminine, the body, sexuality and sensuality, and nature. Freud had difficulty interpreting Jung's dreams when they analyzed each other while traveling together to America in 1909, especially Jung's dreams containing many collective contents and symbolic images. The best example is Jung's house-of-many-levels dream where he started on the second floor of "his" home decorated in an antiquated style. He descended to a much older first floor of the fifteenth or sixteenth century with Medieval furnishings, then down into an ancient Roman-period basement. A tunnel went down from the basement floor to a "low cave cut into the rock" containing disintegrating human bones and broken pottery. (MDR, p. 158-160) That dream gave Jung his first idea of a collective unconscious with layers of cultural history atop a foundation of primitive man with an animal soul. (p. 160)

During this period Jung was becoming keenly aware of the difference between his intellectual attitude and Freud's. Jung was steeped in history and philosophy, especially the eighteenth and nineteenth century writers who were related to the atmosphere of the first-story salon of his layered house dream. Jung felt that Freud, by comparison, was rather shallow in that realm, dominated by an anti-religious Enlightenment perspective and soul-constricting "scientific materialism." He had an "almost exclusive personalism" that did not account for general historical forces. (MDR, p. 161) Jung was of the Romantic tradition that arose in response to the Enlightenment and the ills of the Industrial Revolution. (See Appendix A: William Blake and the English Romantics)

Disappointed with Freud's "reasonable solution," Jung felt that "people who know nothing about nature are of course neurotic, for they are not adapted to reality," not knowing "they are human beings like all others." He felt he had internalized this sense by growing up in the country with peasants, where sexual jokes and fantasies in folklore, incest, perversions and criminality, showed him "only too plainly the ugliness and meaninglessness of human existence." "City folks," Jung added, "know nothing about nature and the human stable." All of Freud's brilliant work "had apparently succeeded in finding nothing more in the depths of the psyche than the all too familiar and 'all-too-human' limitations." (MDR, p.166)

Jung said one shouldn't just attack a person's defenses; there has to be something positive to replace the neurotic sense of self that gets exposed in analysis. (MDR, p. 166) The unconscious is not just the seething caldron of the Id, but also the source of the heights and depths of the human spirit—the arts, sciences, great religions, and creativity. This is an important ecopsychological perspective, for how we view the unconscious affects how we view our relationship with nature.

In contrast to Freud, Jung believed every psychic event has both a causal *and* a goal-oriented dimension. Jung emphasized the purposive, healing tendencies in the unconscious over an analytical search for the causal derivation of the disturbance. He used dreams as a major vehicle in this approach, an approach misunderstood because of its subtle middle position between the poles of spirit and matter, the objective and subjective levels, and the causal/reductive and final/prospective. (von Franz 1975, p. 97) The prospective tendencies in the unconscious are the human experience of the self-organizing tendencies leading towards the integrity of any organism, organic or inorganic. (see Appendix C: Self and Organism in volume 1 of *The Dairy Farmer's Guide*)

Freud's theories were devastating to the feminine psyche. He perceived women to be inferior men, plagued with penis envy because they lacked male genitalia. Women for Freud were as mysterious and dangerously uncontrollable as nature. (see Appendix A in volume 1 of *The Dairy Farmer's Guide*) This view of women was in many respects typical of the Victorian Era. Freud believed his degree of scientific objectivity put him outside the Jewish religion and tradition, but he was unaware of the extent the Jewish worldview colored what he saw in himself and in his female clients. This perspective affected the theoretical formulation he developed while working with his primary clientele—wealthy, neurotic, sexually frustrated and abused Viennese women. It also influenced the interpretation of his own dreams during his self-analysis.

As the founder of psychoanalysis, Freud was never analyzed. He resisted giving Jung personal associations to his dreams for fear of losing his position of authority. (MDR, p. 158) One third of the dreams in Freud's seminal text, *The Interpretation of Dreams*, published in 1900, were Freud's own dreams. That material and what we know about Freud's life and family illustrate Jung's statement that every psychology is a subjective confession. In the end, Jung felt that Freudian psychology was crippled by the neurosis of its founder, a neurosis he was unable to resolve. (p. 167) (n 23)

The house-of-many-levels dream served to revive Jung's interest in archeology, leading to an intensive study of mythology, Gnostic writers, and primitive cultures. He discovered "the close relationship between ancient mythology and the psychology of primitives." (MDR, p. 162) His studies culminated in the publication in 1912 of *Symbols of Transformation* describing how mythological motifs could be found in the psychotic fantasies of a modern Western woman.

CHAPTER 5

Splitting from Freud and the Descent into the Depths

Jung knew he would incur Freud's wrath when he published *Symbols*, which asserted there was a religious aspect of incest that served as a metaphor for the transformation of libido. Incest is one of the prime symbols for the union of opposites, psychologically stated as an intimate, symbiotic relationship between consciousness and the unconscious. In Christianity, for example, Mary becomes bridesmaid to the King of Heaven, none other than her son Jesus. Only in rare cases, Jung believed, was incest a personal complication; it usually had a highly religious aspect as revealed in its "decisive part in almost all cosmologies and in numerous myths. But Freud clung to the literal interpretation of it and could not grasp the spiritual significance of incest as a symbol." (MDR, p. 167) (n 24) The greatest significance of sexuality, for Jung, was as "the expression of the chthonic spirit"—an important concept for ecopsychology—and "the dark side of the God-image." (p. 168) From personal experience and from working with a broader clientele in a state mental hospital, Jung knew that a host of issues besides sexuality could cause mental illness, including problems with prestige, poverty, and "the tragic circumstances of life." (p. 147)

Jung knew how "terribly merciless" and ruthless Freud had been with others who "varied just a little bit, then he was finished," cast out and shunned. (Bair 2003, p. 227) He believed Freud would see his thinking as being "under the domination of a father complex against him" and would understand "my whole work as a personal resistance against himself and sexuality." (p. 233) Publication of *Symbols* in 1912 indeed ended their friendship, although Jung knew it was doomed a year earlier. (Hannah 1991, p. 103) "My book was declared to be rubbish; I was a mystic, and that settled the matter." (MDR, p. 167) (n 25) Freud would say Jung was "immature himself and in need of supervision," (Bair 2003, p. 235) telling devotees Jung was "crazy" and "lacks insight into his illness" (p. 238)—"a perfect fool, he seems to be

Christ himself." (Paskauskas 1993, 108F, Dec. 8, 1912, p. 182 quoted in Bair 2003, p. 725 note 102) (n 26)

Commencing after the psychoanalytic conference in Munich in October, 1913, Jung entered the most confused, frightening and dramatic period of his life. The conference was the last face-to-face confrontation with Freud and the beginning of Jung's ostracism. (Bair 2003, p. 290) Jung was in a state of total disorientation. He felt he had "fallen into an immense hole" (p. 242) with the realization at the conclusion of writing *Symbols* that he and many others no longer found relevance in the Christian myth, and seriously questioned whether there was any myth modern man was living by, particularly himself. (MDR, p. 171) Looking back he said that "the single most important achievement in his life...was that he 'saved [his] life from that hole' and 'didn't drown in it.'" (Bair 2003, p. 242) Jung went on an epic shamanic journey into the perilous depths of the human psyche beginning in the fall of 1913 and extending to the end of 1917. This experience provided the *prima materia* for the rest of his life's work and the basis for all further development of his unique psychological theories, giving his thought a more ecopsychological focus.

Not only was Jung reeling from the final split from Freud and the cultural disturbance in Europe that erupted into World War I in July of 1914; he had begun a relationship with a much younger former patient named Toni Wolff during Emma's pregnancy with their fifth child. That relationship reached an erotic phase in the spring of 1914 around the birth of the child in March. (Bair 2003, p. 248) (n 27) Jung's experiences with Toni Wolff and Sabina Spielrein, a former patient with whom he had had an intimate relationship in 1909 (n 28), later helped him realize the significance of the feminine (the anima) in a man's psyche. (p. 91, 105, 106, 145, 46, 151, 152, 154-57, 181, 191, 194, 688 note 23) Jung was suffering a mid-life crisis, a period he later realized would activate the anima that initially gets projected onto a woman. This created problems typical of the first generation of analysts. They themselves were not analyzed by others, and the sensitive issues of relationships with patients and appropriate boundaries were being discovered through trial and error. Jung later became the first to require those wanting to be analysts to undergo a personal "training" analysis.

The unconscious material in the form of dreams, visions and frightening emotional states was often nightmarish and overwhelming for Jung. In October 1913 after the Munich conference, he had the first of two hour-long visions of monstrous floods of debris and corpses that turned to blood and destroyed northern Europe. (MDR, 175, 176) Around Christmas of 1913 he began having a series of dreams that were to take him further into the depths. He dreamt of a dove that turned into a golden haired girl in the early evening "while the male dove is busy with the twelve dead." (p. 172) He also dreamt of a series of tombs dating back to a crusader's tomb of the twelfth century; the entombed corpses came to life as Jung looked at them intensively. (p. 172, 173) In conjunction with his house-of-many-levels dream, these two dreams taught Jung there were historical dominants in our psyches: a cultural unconscious that was alive and affective in each of us—the archetypes. (p. 173) Later he realized the link between the anima and the deeper levels of the unconscious was portrayed by the relationship of the doves in his two doves dream. The atmosphere in the dove dream and a word association to it made Jung realize he had to re-live his childhood. This released a flood of fantasies that he decided to follow no matter where they would lead. (Bair 2003, p. 244)

"A turning point in my fate," Jung wrote, came when he resigned himself to "the painfully humiliating experience" of reverting to a childhood passion for building houses and castles out of building blocks and stones. He built a whole village on the shoreline of his property in Kusnacht, just south of Zurich. When he found a red stone to use as an altar for the church, he recalled the underground phallus of his childhood dream which he had long since forgotten. (MDR, p. 173, 174)

He pursued his building game with great relish, allocating time every day to play beside the lake. This activity helped him clarify his thoughts and allowed dimly felt fantasies to emerge. Later he carefully wrote down these fantasies in the *Black Books* as the basis for reflection and research. The building game was engaged with "the inner certainty that I was on the way to discovering my own myth." (p. 174, 175)

In the midst of this intense preoccupation with the images from the unconscious, Jung withdrew from eight years of lecturing at the University. "My experience and experiments with the unconscious had brought my intellectual activity to a standstill," he said. His unconscious material had struck him dumb. Jung felt he "would first have to find an entirely new and different orientation" if he were to instruct students. (MDR, p. 193) "I knew that it would fill my life, and for the sake of that goal I was ready to take any kind of risk." (p. 194) By the end of 1913 he had given up diagnostic categories, particularly Freud's, and made no interpretations of his patients' dreams based on his earlier writings. Instead he asked simple, direct questions, inquiring of the patients what they thought the material meant, noticing that an "interpretation came to light all by itself" in a kind of "self-healing" and integrated manner. (Bair 2003, p. 246, 247) (Self-organizing functions are a central element of dynamic systems theory. See Appendix B: Bootstrapping the Archetypes in volume 3 of *The Dairy Farmer's Guide*)

Jung took a decisive step in December of 1913, letting himself sink into his fears and feeling himself plunging into the depths. He had a vision of the death and renewal of the hero/sun, with the abnormal occurrence of an enormous outpouring of blood at the end. Six days later he dreamt that he and a brown-skinned savage ambushed and killed the Teutonic hero Siegfried as he rode in his chariot made of the bones of the dead. Jung felt disgusted and remorseful for having destroyed something so great and beautiful. (MDR, p. 179, 180) Siegfried represented the German desire to heroically impose their will on the world, and Jung recognized his secret identity with him; it was as if Jung himself had been shot. He realized he had to abandon his identity with his heroic idealism and bow to something higher than the ego's will. (p. 180, 181) (n 29)

Jung's dream of the destruction of the heroic ego stance was a necessary first step toward developing a healthy relationship with the unconscious. This change extends upward and outward to a mutually beneficial relationship with others and a sustainable relationship with the environment. The initial and deepest changes begin within, or are simultaneous with, inner change. Westerners, especially males, have a strong cultural identity with the archetype of the hero imposing his will over unruly nature, as was Freud's position. (see Appendix A of volume 1 of *The Dairy Farmer's Guide*)

Jung's next major step began by imagining a steep descent. At the bottom, he found himself on the edge of a cosmic abyss with an otherworldly feeling of being in the land of the dead. There he discovered an old man named Elijah together with a beautiful, young, blind girl named Salome. Elijah said they belonged together since eternity. A black serpent living with them displayed a fondness for Jung. Jung talked to them as though they were real people, having a long conversation with Elijah that Jung did not understand. Elijah seemed reasonable, with a clear intelligence, but Jung was distinctly suspicious of Salome. (MDR, p.181, 182; see the first paragraph of Appendix F)

Salome was an anima figure, an erotic element who personified Eros; "blind because she does not see the meaning of things." (see Appendix

E in volume 3 for blindness and the archetypal feminine) Elijah was a wise old prophet who personified Logos, "represent[ing] the factor of intelligence and knowledge." (MDR, p. 182) Jung was just beginning to live out his relationship with Toni Wolff who was 13 years his junior. (Hannah 1991, p. 117) (n 30) Jung later recognized an old man accompanied by a young girl was a frequent dream motif, also found in myths. (n 31) The large black snake is often the counterpart of the hero in myths, who has snake eyes or a snake mother, or changes into a revered snake after death. (MDR, p. 182) (n 32)

A significant omission from Jung's autobiography is the account of his second descent into the unconscious a few nights after the first descent. In that active imagination he saw Salome worshipping him as the Christ, believing Jung could cure her blindness. A female snake coiled around Jung up to his heart. As Jung struggled he "assumed the attitude of the Crucifixion" (Jung 1989, p. 96 quoted in Noll 1992, p. 23) and felt his face become that of a lion or tiger. Salome arose and could see.

Jung believed he had experienced "the mystery of deification"; that he had become Aion (Jung 1989, p. 97 quoted in Noll 1992, p. 23), "the supreme god of the Mithraic hierarchy [who] creates and destroys all things." (CW 18, ¶ 266) He thought "the symbolic rite of deification played a part in [the ancient] mysteries" and in the Mithraic initiation the initiate becomes "a vessel in which the opposites reconcile." (Jung 1989, p. 99 quoted in Noll 1992, p. 24) (see Appendix F: Jung and Mithraism for the development of this topic)

CHAPTER 6

Philemon and the Discovery of the Inner Woman

An evolution of the Elijah and Aion figures soon arose in one of Jung's dreams. He dreamt of "an old man with the horns of a bull. He held a bunch of four keys, one of which he clutched as if he were about to open a lock. He had the wings of the kingfisher with its characteristic colors." (MDR, p. 182, 183) Jung called him Philemon and he soon began to dominate Jung's visions as a pagan figure with a Gnostic coloration and Egyptian and Greek Hellenistic elements. Philemon was an integration of the spiritual and chthonic domains: wings represent the air, the spirit, while bull horns are phallic and chthonic masculine. The kingfisher, relating to the Fisher-King in the Grail legend, is a bird that dives into water to catch fish, symbolic of the contents of the unconscious.

Philemon and other figures in Jung's fantasies taught him a seminal concept—the objective reality of the psyche. In his active imagination fantasies, Jung held long conversations with Philemon who said things that Jung would not have consciously thought of. Philemon said Jung "treated thoughts as if [he] generated them [himself]...' If you should see people in a room, you would not think that you had made those people, or that you were responsible for them.'" (MDR, p. 183)

Philemon became Jung's spiritual guru, representing superior insight, guiding him on his journey through the depths of the unconscious. At times this mysterious figure seemed quite real, "as if he were a living personality. I went walking up and down the garden with him," Jung wrote. (MDR, p. 183) He was pleased to discover 15 years later that some Hindus have a spirit for a teacher. (p. 184)

Jung began to fear there would be an endless procession of personifications when yet another figure followed Philemon, one he called Ka, a name used by the ancient Egyptians for the earthly form, or the embodied soul, of a person. The ka-soul appeared in Jung's fantasy coming up from the earth as if out of a deep shaft. Jung painted him as a herm (phallic shaped object) with a stone base and a bronze upper part. (see Appendix H: Jung's Phallic Self Image) A kingfisher's wing appeared in the upper part of the painting with a round, glowing nebula of stars between it and the head of Ka. There was something demonic, Mephistophelian, in Ka. Holding a pagoda or reliquary and stylus to work on it, Ka said it was he "'who buries the gods in gold and gems.'" (MDR, p. 185)

Jung eventually integrated both figures through his study of alchemy (MDR, p. 185), a symbolic base for ecopsychology. Philemon was a winged spirit representing "the spiritual aspect, or 'meaning.'" Ka was a kind of earth or metal demon representing the spirit in nature, like the gnomes and Greek Dactyls or the alchemical Mercurius as the spirit of quicksilver. (MDR, p. 185) The Philemon-Ka association is a spirit-chthonic relationship. Philemon had a wounded foot that could be seen as an Eros wound that initiates one into life, sex, and death, from which wisdom can arise (see Hexagram 44 in the *I Ching*, Coming to Meet in Wilhelm 1967, p. 170-173). Jung's relationship with Toni Wolff was for him a deeply personal experience of the Eros wound that intensely complicates life as it enlivens it. Ka makes everything real but also obscures Meaning or replaces it "by beauty, the 'eternal reflection.'" (p. 185) Ka as trickster can deceive and detract one from the spiritual path with intellectual cleverness and the dazzling beauty and fascination with the unconscious and its products.

In the spring and early summer of 1914, during the heightened erotic phase with Toni Wolff, Jung had three visions of Arctic cold waves descending over Europe in mid-summer, killing everything. (n 33) In the last of these visions the leaves on a tree "had been transformed by the effects of frost into sweet grapes full of healing juices," demonstrating the healing and transformative element that can emerge from the unconscious. "[Jung] plucked the grapes and gave them to a large, waiting crowd." (MDR, p. 176)

During this time, Jung lived in a state of constant tension, fearing "a psychic disturbance within" (MDR, p. 173):

> Often I felt as if gigantic blocks of stone were tumbling down upon me...But there was a demonic strength in me, and from the beginning there was no doubt in my mind that I must find the meaning of what I was experiencing in these fantasies...I had an unswerving conviction that I was obeying a higher will. (p. 177)

He was frequently so overwrought he did yoga exercises to calm himself enough to resume working with the unconscious. (MDR, p. 173) (n 34) Central to his process was a technique for engaging powerful emotional states, a process of "listening for the personal mythology," later called "active imagination." It was Jung's first technique that differed from Freud's. (Bair 2003, p. 246) Instead of yielding to an emotion and becoming possessed by it, Jung objectified the emotion by getting it to present itself as an image or having it tell him what it wanted. (MDR, p. 177; Hannah 1991, p. 108). (see chapter 2 note 77 of volume 1 of *The Dairy Farmer's Guide*) Others have described the process as "riding the wild horse"—instead of *being* the horse/wild emotion, one is in intimate *relationship* to it. Both horse and rider can be changed by the interaction. (n 35)

After the outbreak of World War I at the end of July, 1914, Jung gave priority to working on the fantasies he recorded in the *Black Books* because, he said, "I had to try to understand what had happened and to what extent my own experience coincided with that of mankind in general." (MDR, p. 176) He analyzed the psychic conditions under which the fantasies occurred and enhanced the fantasies with drawings. Each entry in his notebook was an "experiment of personal confrontation with [his] soul." (Bair 2003, p. 245, 246)] "Sometimes it was as if I were hearing it with my ears," Jung wrote, "sometimes feeling it with my mouth, as if my tongue were formulating words; now and then I heard myself whispering aloud"—all forms of active imagination. (MDR, p. 178)

Jung later began work on the *Red Book* to expand on the dreams and fantasies recorded in the *Black Books* along with the words spoken to him by Philemon. (MDR, p. 188) In addition to the mandalas Jung painted, many of the paintings "may best be regarded as active imaginations in their own right." (Shamdasani 2005, p. 99) He lavishly illustrated his fantasies and developed a unique script to provide an interpretive text. (MDR, p. 188 note 6) (n 36)

Toni Wolff became Jung's spiritual and intellectual companion. (Bair 2003, p. 321, 322) (n 37) She was allowed to watch his lakeside building games and was the only person in early 1914 to read the *Black Books* and discuss its contents with Jung. (p. 249) (n 38) She had a natural affinity for the type of "non-neurotic psychoanalysis" Jung was developing. (p. 266) Her active mind and wide ranging interests mirrored Jung's, allowing her to serve as his *sora mystica* and *femme inspiratrice*. They were constantly together during the most tumultuous phase of Jung's "confrontation with the unconscious" and Jung was forever grateful: he doubted he could have made it without her. He felt extremely lonely since there was no one other than her to talk to about these strange experiences. She offered unfailing sympathy and understanding, never flinching at the occasionally bizarre material from Jung's, or others', unconscious. (Hannah 1991, p. 119, 120)

Jung told Emma he had to treat Toni like his "other wife" and got so confused on how to treat each equally and respectfully he once contemplated drowning himself. (Bair 2003, p. 266) He was filled with anguish over his adulterous behavior but felt the situation was beyond his control, saying he was in "the midst of the anima problem." (p. 248) The three eventually managed to work out an uneasy truce. (p. 314; Hannah 1991, p. 119, 120) (n 39)

Jung had discovered the anima, the inner feminine of a man, when he began to record his thoughts and fantasies in the *Black Books*. He heard a female voice within who contradicted his feeling that his drawings were not art. He retorted against her position and she responded again in defense. Realizing that the "woman within" had no speech center, he offered her *his* speech and she came through with a long statement. (MDR, p. 185, 186) Jung recognized the voice as that of a patient (Maria Moltzer) who became "a living figure within my mind." (p. 185) (n 40)

At first Jung "felt a little awed by [the anima]. It was like the feeling of an invisible presence in the room." He conscientiously wrote every evening so his anima would help him retrieve his fantasies. He said it was like writing to "a part of myself with a different viewpoint from my conscious one. I got remarks of an unusual and unexpected character. I was like a patient in analysis with a ghost [Philemon] and a woman!" (MDR, p. 186)

It is fairly easy for the psyche to personify its contents because they have relative autonomy with "a separate identity of their own." (MDR, p. 187) The psyche by nature produces images. Many are fearful of a living "It" (the translation of Freud's Id) within themselves, but personification of unconscious contents releases consciousness from the secret grip of the unconscious and allows for an interaction and relationship between the two. (p. 187) (n 41) Jung developed means of communicating with the unconscious by sandplay, painting, detailed writing out of fantasies, sculpturing in stone: such processes he would come to call active imagination. (n 42)

Jung described a man's inner feminine, the anima, and a woman's inner male side, the animus, as the "archetype of the soul." Because a man's feminine nature is more deeply unconscious than his conscious self-identification as a man, the anima is associated with the deeper levels of the unconscious. This gives the anima a strong historical character that personifies the cultural and prehistoric unconscious still alive in the psyche (the two doves dream). (MDR, p. 286) At their deeper and more profound levels the anima and animus are personifications of one's soul and function as the mediatrix and guide to one's spiritual depths. Pursuing these ideas, Jungian analyst James Hillman resurrected a Western neo-Platonic idea of Aphrodite as the Soul of the World that has important implications for ecopsychology. (see Appendix H in volume 3 of *The Dairy Farmer's Guide*)

Jung initially projected his positive anima function onto Toni Wolff, who helped him connect his ego to the deeper levels of his unconscious through her feel for its processes and paths. (n 43) In that form she served as the transformative aspect of the anima (see Appendix G: The Sacred Prostitute and the Erotic Feminine in volume 3 of *The Dairy Farmer's Guide*) in relation to the dark aspect of the Goddess associated with heightened sensuality, the death-and-rebirth motif in the psyche and in nature, and enlightenment through non-reproductive sexuality. (see Appendix H: The Black Goddess in volume 3) Emma embodied the anima as Jung's supportive and nurturing mother figure.

Jung's self-analysis proceeded with the help of an inner male spirit guide (Philemon), an intimate emotional relationship with an inner feminine presence that often appeared as a confrontive negative anima figure, and the aid of a positive anima figure in the person of Toni Wolff. Contrast this with Freud's severe intellectual self-analysis in *The Interpretation of Dreams* where he reduced everything to the *biological* sex drive.

The anima is perhaps the most difficult aspect of the psyche for a man to recognize and come to terms with. (Hannah 1991, p. 125) A woman with traits similar enough to a man's anima acts like a movie screen in drawing out an unconscious projection of his inner feminine onto her. The challenge for the man is to recognize and withdraw the projection to its source, his own unconscious, and deal with it as an inner figure while seeing the feminine traits as aspects of himself. This frees the outer woman to be seen for who she really is, not constrained by what is being projected onto her in terms of expected behaviors and attitudes peculiar to the man's anima. (n 44) If a man remains unconscious of the projection he acts as if possessed by the anima; it is as if he is a poorly developed woman who may be highly emotional, overly sentimental, wildly intuitive, extremely irrational, etc.

Often the anima initially appears in a negative form as an inner force that counters the ego position. At first Jung was unaware of his inner art critic, so his unconscious projected this anima onto a woman who held such a view, Maria Moltzer. He then deliberately used her voice in active imagination to bring to consciousness that perspective, discovering in the process the concepts of the anima and projection. (Hannah 1991, p. 124) As Jung more clearly came to recognize the anima as an inner figure both positive and negative, he said "he became less dependent on the mediation of the outer woman" to connect him to his unconscious. (p. 125) Eventually Jung became directly conscious of the anima's ideas because he learned to accept and understand the contents of the unconscious and how to behave towards the inner images. He could read meaning from the unconscious directly from the dreams and no longer needed a mediator to communicate them. (MDR, p. 188) This moved him closer to experiencing the meaning of the Chinese ideogram for the sage—"The ear listening to the inner King." Von Franz saw Jung's feminine side in how he was affected by "the suffering in the contemporary world, the devastation of nature, the overpopulation problem, the war, the rape of still flourishing non-Christian cultures by the brutality of modern technology." (von Franz 1975, p. 145) (n 45)

Jung knew he was dealing with "the stuff of psychosis" which confuses the mental patient, but he also recognized this realm as "the matrix of a mythopoetic imagination which has vanished from our rational age." This imagination is everywhere present, but journeying into "the other pole of the world" is considered to be risky and dangerous. (MDR, p. 188, 189) It leads to "a struggle against the sanity-threatening danger of fascination by the measureless heights and depths and paradoxes of psychic truth." (CW 13, ¶ 210) Gnosticism, philosophical alchemy, *Faust*, and *Zarathustra* are descriptions of this journey into the mythopoetic dimension of the psyche. (MDR, p. 189) It is a taboo journey for conservative Christians because the alchemists viewed Christ as only one reflection of the inner Anthropos—the inner cosmic being. (CW 13, ¶ 210) (see Appendix C) Many Christians think it is heretical to talk about any spiritual experience outside of a Christian context while the alchemists had a thousand "indecipherable secret names" for their central mystery. (Hannah 1991, p. 114)

During the intense work with his fantasies, Jung strongly felt the need for a sense of "this world" and reality to keep him from going insane. He got that from his family, professional work, and annual military service required of all Swiss men. (MDR, p. 189) (n 46) Jung emphasized, "it is impossible to face the strange world of the unconscious unless the foundations of consciousness are well and truly laid." (Hannah 1991, p. 134) (n 47) He wrote, "No matter how deeply absorbed or how blown about I was, I always knew that everything I was experiencing was ultimately directed at this real life of mine. I meant to meet its obligations and fulfill its meanings." (MDR, p. 189)

By the end of January, 1916 the contents of Jung's unconscious had become activated to the point of bursting out. (n 48) His collaboration with Toni Wolff in a professional and erotic capacity was reaching its peak. The marital tension affected the children, now old enough to resent Wolff's seemingly continual presence with their father behind closed doors in their own home. (Bair 2003, p. 293) It may have been the third time Emma threatened divorce. (p. 266)

Jung began the 1916 descent into the unconscious with a fantasy of his soul flying away. This signified a withdrawal into the unconscious, the realm of the dead, recalling Jung's dream of the dove/young girl whose male partner worked at night with the twelve dead. The anima, or soul in a man, is what establishes a relationship with the deeper layers of the unconscious and Toni Wolff was still carrying an important part of that function for him. The unconscious in a certain sense represents the collectivity of the dead: the realm of the ancestors who gave us our genetic and cultural heritage. When the soul withdraws into the unconscious, "it produces a mysterious animation and gives visible form to the ancestral traces, the collective contents [the archetypes]. Like a medium, it gives the dead a chance to manifest themselves." (MDR, p. 191) (This is why respect and worship of the ancestors and the sacredness of burial sites is so important to indigenous cultures.) The depth of the unconscious Jung was experiencing in 1916 revealed what he called the "psychoid" dimension of the archetype where synchronicities happen. The "manifestation of the dead" he was about to experience is a most bizarre account for a scientific, Western mind. Paranormal events occur when one is in a strong emotional state associated with an archetypal constellation. "What a dreary world it would be if the rules were not violated sometimes," Jung remarked. (p. 191)

After the outlines of an inner change gradually began to occur, followed by the fantasy of his soul flying away, Jung began to feel restless. He sensed an ominous atmosphere around him: "I had the strange feeling that the air was filled with ghostly entities. Then it was as if my house began to be haunted." (MDR, p. 190) A daughter saw a white figure passing through her room. Another daughter twice had her blanket snatched away at night. That same night his nine-year-old son had a terrible anxiety dream of a fisherman catching a fish belonging to the Devil. The son's drawing of the fisherman looked uncannily like Jung's drawing of Philemon in his secret *Red Book*. (Bair 2003, p. 294) Two days later the doorbell began to ring frantically, but no one was there. "The atmosphere was thick...The whole house was filled as if it were a crowd present, crammed full of spirits." Jung shouted out, "For God's sake, what in the world is this?" (MDR, 190, 191) He heard a chorus in his mind reply, "We have come back from Jerusalem where we found not what we sought." This became the opening line for a bizarre text, *The Seven Sermons to the Dead*, that flowed out of Jung in a frenzy of writing over the course of the next three evenings. "As soon as I took up the pen, the whole ghostly assemblage evaporated," Jung wrote. "The room quieted and the atmosphere cleared. The haunting was over." (MDR, p. 191)

The hauntings were the first of several parapsychological experiences in Jung's life that he came to recognize "as a pre-stage to a creative effort," usually occurring "before he realized he was going to write." If Jung neglected the unconscious, uncanny effects would be felt in the surrounding environment such as those his family experienced before his writing of the *Seven Sermons*. (Hannah 1991, p. 121) (n 49) Not only did the writings dispel the hauntings, but harmony and stasis returned to the family "as his children and Emma grudgingly accepted Toni Wolff's presence in their lives." (Bair 2003, p. 297) (n 50) Parapsychological phenomena suggest a dimension of relationship to the environment beyond current scientific concepts.

Jungian scholar Sonu Shamdasani describes the *Sermons* as "an outline of a psychocosmology written in a literary and symbolic style... a preliminary synthesis of the points that Jung had been slowly working towards in the *Black Books* and in the *Red Book*." They were "the first account of many important themes which would preoccupy Jung throughout his later work." (Shamdasani 2005, p. 100-102) The writings explored the individual's relationship with the collective unconscious (presented in the *Sermons* as multiple gods and the Gnostic god Abraxas of many and varied traits); what he would come to call the "individuation process"; the possibility of evil in God; the powerful sexual dimension of his developing concepts of anima and animus; and finally a rejection of Abraxas and an "embrace of a single god who will lead to ultimate redemption." (Bair 2003, p. 296) The *Sermons* foreshadowed Jung's moving beyond Gnosticism and his eventual discovery of the Self. They helped him relate to the spirit of antiquity in order to begin to understand the transition to Christianity as illustrated by the contrast between Pompeii and Christian Rome. (p. 296)

The *Sermons* were the culmination of a series of dreams and experiences dating back to Jung's childhood phallic nightmare and they led him to a new and deeper perspective:

> From that time on, the dead have become ever more distinct for me as the voices of the Unanswered, Unresolved, and Unredeemed; for since the questions and demands which my destiny required me to answer did not come from outside, they must have come from the inner world. (MDR, p. 191, 192)

Jung was beginning to focus on the unanswered archetypal problems in our Judeo-Christian heritage, particularly on the turning point of the repression and suppression of paganism and Gnosticism in early Christian Rome.

Writing the *Seven Sermons* in 1916 marked the end of Jung's major work with the *Red Book* although he continued with it until he became seriously involved with alchemy around 1930. (Bair 2003, p. 293-297, 399; Shamdasani 2005, p. 102) An important function of the book had been to record and elaborate on Philemon's autonomous thoughts, but in the *Seven Sermons* Jung was speaking for himself albeit in an archaic manner. The *Red Book* had turned into an elaborate aesthetic development of fantasies, a mixture "of fantasy and prophecy," that emerged from his interactions with the anima, Philemon, and Toni Wolff. (Bair 2003, p. 396) (n 51) To wholly return to reality from the realm presented in the *Red Book* and the *Seven Sermons*, he began a lifelong "rigorous process of understanding" the manifestations of the unconscious and taking up a position toward it. (MDR, p. 188) The work entailed translation of the material revealed by the unconscious into psychological language, as well as researching and explaining the motifs of unconscious imagery in terms of recurring themes/archetypes. These motifs are revealed in the religions, rituals, myths, symbols and the classics of art and literature throughout the world. At the end of 1917 Jung decided to suppress The *Red Book* and the *Seven Sermons*, fearing the material was too raw and bizarre to present to the public. His attention shifted even more to shaping his insights into a form that could be presented to the world. (Bair 295, 297)

Jung recognized elements in his images that were not simply personal: "It was then that I ceased to belong to myself alone," he wrote. He knew he had to undergo the original experience because there was no description of it at the time. He rededicated himself to planting the wealth of his subjective experiences into a broader reality, saying it was the only way

> of extricating myself from that chaos...I took great care to try to understand every single image, every item of my psychic inventory, and to classify them scientifically—so far as this was possible—and, above all, to realize them in actual life. (MDR, p. 192)

Unprocessed knowledge gained from insight into powerful fantasies can be dangerous. Not understanding the nature and dimensions of archetypal powers in the unconscious and their relationship to each other leads to fragmentation of the psyche. The great power from association with archetypal energies is seductive to the individual experiencing them and to those around that individual.

Since archetypes have positive and negative aspects, Jung insisted it was necessary to take an ethical position vis-à-vis what comes forth from the unconscious. He believed "the images of the unconscious place a great responsibility upon a man." (MDR, p. 193) The energies must be realized and given form in one's life, not left in the realm of fantasy. The unconscious gets projected onto others and one can become conscious by realizing that the projections are aspects of oneself. The tests and trials of reality and relationships are grist for the mill for processing and reflection, the lab and library work of the alchemists. "You cannot individuate on Mt. Everest!" Jung liked to say. (Hannah 1991, p. 130)

CHAPTER 7

Discovery of the Self

Jung was preoccupied with images from his unconscious from 1913 to 1917, which had been most intense and profound from 1913 through 1915 (Bair 2003, p. 254)—from the post-Munich conference to the *Sermons* in January of 1916. The stream of fantasies then slowly ebbed away. "Not until it had subsided and I was no longer held captive inside the magic mountain was I able to take an objective view of that whole experience and begin to reflect upon it," Jung wrote. (MDR, p. 206, 207) He often stated his confrontation with the unconscious "was incomparably the hardest task he ever undertook." (Hannah 1991, p. 127)

He had gradually begun to emerge from the darkness of his "creative confrontation with the unconscious" towards the end of World War I in 1918-1919. He attributed this emergence to a daily practice of making circular drawings that seemed to correspond to his inner situation at the time. The sequence of drawings helped him observe his psychic transformations from day to day. Jung later realized his personal drawings corresponded to sacred circular drawings in the East called mandalas. (see Appendix B: The Mandala) Each mandala he drew was a "cryptogram" of the state of the self for that day and they led to the discovery of what he called the archetype of the Self. (MDR, p. 196) From this experience arose Jung's belief that the goal of psychic development is the realization and attunement with the Self—the wholeness of personality. The mandala is an expression of the Self that is the exponent of all paths of life; all paths in life can be traced back to the point in the center—the Source. Linear and uniform development exists mostly at the beginning of life; all else is circumambulation about one's center, the Self. (p. 196, 197)

Jung's experience revealed a fundamental aspect of the ecopsychological matrix: the mandala is the microcosm, the world within, mirroring the macrocosm, the world without. "As above, so below" the alchemists said. (n 52) This concept is central to establishing an ecopsychological base that links psychological theories with environmental and ecological perspectives. The ego's position and goal-directedness is subordinate to Self if the psyche is harmonious and well-functioning. The Chinese ideogram for the sage conveys this well: "The ear listening to the Inner King." At the cultural level the Self is expressed as Jesus, Buddha, Allah, Yahweh, the Tao, *Wakan Tanka*, etc. Jung proclaimed: "I knew that in finding the mandala as an expression of the self I had attained what was for me the ultimate." His insight about the self gave him stability and a gradual return to inner peace. (MDR, p. 197)

In 1927, about nine years after Jung made the first daily mandala drawings, he had a dream that confirmed his ideas about the center and the Self. Jung dreamt he was with some Swiss people in a dirty, sooty city—Liverpool. It was a dark, dismal, rainy winter night, representing his psychological situation at the time—"extremely unpleasant, black and opaque":

> We found a broad square dimly illuminated by street lights, into which many streets converged. The various quarters of the city were arranged radially around the square. In the center was a round pool, and in the middle of it a small island. While everything round about was obscured by rain, fog, smoke, and dimly lit darkness, the little island blazed with sunlight. On it stood a single tree, a magnolia, in a shower of reddish blossoms. It was as though the tree stood in the sunlight and were at the same time the source of light. (MDR, p. 198)

Only Jung saw the beautiful tree on its sunlit island. "The individual quarters of the city were themselves arranged radially around a central point," Jung added. "This point formed a small open square illuminated by a larger street lamp, and constituted a small replica of the island." (p. 198) Jung told Barbara Hannah:

> The great discovery of this dream, that he illustrated with a painting [CW 13, plate A. 3], was that the "other Swiss" lived in the "vicinity of one of these secondary centers" and not near the center of the whole mandala. This was his first vivid image of the nature of the Self, which is collective in the main central island (open and accessible to all who are able to see it) and individual in the small unique replica, where, like the "other Swiss," each of us must live. He thus first learned that our place is not in the center of the mandala, but at the side, in a small individual replica of our own. He thus began to distinguish his own personal

myth from the myth of modern man. (Hannah 1991, p. 185)

Jung later articulated that the myth for modern man is to complete God's creation by "becoming conscious of *all we can* and thus to give [creation] 'objective existence.'" (Hannah 1991, p. 185) (n 53) The fact that Jung's companions could not see the island,

> or apparently become conscious of its existence, taught him that his own individual myth had to do with becoming conscious of the center of all, as well as of everything concerning his own individual replica and the relation between the two. The former constitutes a kind of image of the destiny of mankind in general, the latter of each individual. The constituents are all in the central image, but the selection and combination of these constituents are different, even unique, in each individual replica. (p. 185, 186) (n 54)

The dream also clarified Jung's task as an analyst:

> He knew then that everyone who came to him came for more consciousness, in some form or other—for that is the general myth of mankind in our day—but that the level of consciousness and the things each patient needed to become conscious of were different. The majority—like Jung's Swiss companions in the dream—have as yet no inkling of the existence of the central island. Their task—and often it is all that is asked of them—is to become conscious of things which others seem to have known long ago. (p. 186)

Out of his dismal psychological situation, Jung "had a vision of unearthly beauty," which he said, "was why I was able to live at all. Liverpool is the 'pool of life.' The 'liver,' according to an old view, is the seat of life—that which 'makes to live.'" (MDR, p. 198) Jung had been suffering from depression upon his return from a transformative trip into the primal depths of Africa only to be thrust back into the highly charged atmosphere in Europe between the world wars. After the Liverpool dream biographer Barbara Hannah observed,

> however hopeless things seemed ...Jung was never tempted to despair. He knew there was a light at the center of every individual life, even a sunlit island—where the opposites are harmoniously united...however lost [the world] appears to be in misunderstanding, unconsciousness, and strife. (Hannah 1991, p. 186)

The tree in the center with its own source of light in the darkness is a development of Jung's childhood dream where the phallus, which Jung initially thought was a tree trunk, had its own light, the phallus being an archetypal image of a generative source. The frightening phallus was underground, deep in the unconscious and near its archaic base. Jung's childhood and adolescent Personality No. 2 was an archetypal world of the wholeness of nature removed from humanity—Jung's escape from the vanities and problems of his life and of humankind. The magnolia in the Liverpool dream was a fully developed and blossoming tree *above ground* in a city, within a human matrix. (n 55) This may be attributed to the development of Jung's Eros beginning with his marriage to Emma who offered a nurturing, mothering, containing anima and his relationships with Sabina Spielrein and Toni Wolff who presented the arousing and transforming Aphrodite aspect of the anima. (see Appendix D: The Sacred Prostitute and the Erotic Feminine in volume 3) His anima/Eros would have undergone further development as Jung exercised his model of psychoanalysis where the analyst is transformed by deep psychological work with an analysand. By 1927, when Jung had the Liverpool dream, he was 52 years old and had been a practicing psychiatrist for 27 years, undergoing radical transformations throughout his career. His personal image of the archetype of the Self in the Liverpool dream was central to his enlightenment and his reconnection with humankind.

The magnolia tree was growing on an island in a round pool within a square. The tree is a universal symbol of the Self. (n 56) It unites the three realms it grows in—earth (especially the underground), the human level, and the sky. Trees can attain a great age, and bear with dignity the wounds of their lives that give them character. A tree and not a fairy godmother is the Self symbol in the Grimm's version of "Cinderella." A square in a circle or surrounding a circle touches the circle at four points, four being a number of wholeness. The circle and square touch-points symbolize where the eternal enters space-time with the square symbolizing the manifestation in time and space of what was inspired and guided by the spirit symbolized by the circle. The One manifests by differentiation into the many as in the secondary centers in Jung's dream (the relationship between Hexagrams 1and 2 in the *I Ching*). (n 57) The secondary centers were lit by large streetlights, i.e., man-made lights symbolizing consciousness. Consciousness illuminates and reveals the inner Self, facilitating the manifestation of the eternal into space and time.

Jung said his Liverpool dream

> brought with it a sense of finality. I saw that here the goal
> had been revealed. One could not go beyond the center.
> The center is the goal, and everything is directed toward
> that center. Through this dream I understood that the self
> is the principle and archetype of orientation and mean-
> ing. Therein lies its healing function...Out of it emerged a
> first inkling of my personal myth...The dream depicted the
> climax of the whole process of development of conscious-
> ness. (MDR, p. 198, 199)

He experienced the dream as "an act of grace"—a definitive, clarify-
ing response to the darkness and confusion he was plunged into after
leaving Freud. It conveyed an "objective view of the things that filled
my whole being" without which he said, "I might perhaps have lost
my orientation and been compelled to abandon my undertaking." (p.
199)

Jung's understanding of the Liverpool dream was a clear response
to, and the antithesis of, Freud's concept of the human as being at
best a "normal neurotic." Freud's system was a personal psychology
with a "reasonable solution" to life's issues and "all-too-human" limitations. Jung's formulation was of a person journeying through life on a
path with heart and meaning guided by "the ear listening to the Inner
King"—an Inner King rooted in, and emerging out of, nature.

Jung painted a few more mandalas after the Liverpool dream,
including, a year later, one with a golden castle in the center. The form
and choice of colors gave the painting a Chinese flavor. A remarkable
synchronicity occurred shortly afterward when Jung said he "received
a letter from Richard Wilhelm enclosing the manuscript of a Taoist-
alchemical treatise entitled *The Secret of the Golden Flower*, with a
request that I write a commentary on it." Wilhelm had translated into
German a 2000 year-old Chinese text on the yellow castle, the germ of
the immortal body:

> The text gave me undreamed-of confirmation of my ideas
> about the mandala and the circumambulation of the
> center. That was the first event which broke through my
> isolation. I became aware of an affinity; I could establish
> ties with something and someone. (MDR, p. 197)

Jung said the results of his work to that point had been inconclusive
because they lacked comparison to other material whereas Wilhelm's

Golden Flower contained collaborative material about the collective unconscious. (CW 13, p. 3, 4) (n 58)

Jung told Barbara Hannah that after finding the mandala as the symbol of the Self he once again had to live both personalities but differently from before. He was mostly unconscious of his two personalities when he was a child; when he was conscious of it he experienced it as a terrible conflict. He experienced an inner harmony when he realized the proper relationship between the ego and the center of the psyche, the Self:

> Jung still lived his No. 1 personality and accepted all the responsibilities involved, but his real life was lived, not by himself, but by his greater No. 2 personality. Or, as he once expressed it, "One could say that every evening I go to the bottom of the river where the meaningful life is lived, but in the morning I get up and put on the persona of Dr. Jung and try to live that also as fully as possible." He learned more and more, as the years went on, that this is essentially not two but one. (Hannah 1991, p. 138)

His first major work following his three-year "creative confrontation with the unconscious" was *Psychological Types* published in 1921. Jung explained how "one's psychological type...from the outset determines and limits a person's judgment...An individual is conditioned by his personality type [in how he or she relates to the world] and...every point of view is necessarily relative." (MDR, p. 207) This formulation underscores the difficulty of trying to develop an objective position on anything.

Jung distinguished between introverts and extraverts and classified people as being combinations of thinking, feeling, sensation (orientation to details) or intuitive types. This concept is related to the Native American idea that one is born into a particular point/perspective on the medicine wheel (Storm 1973, p. 6, 7) and the astrological concept of one's birth chart determining one's psychological nature. Jung wrote, "This raised the question of the unity which must compensate this diversity, and it led me directly to the Chinese concept of Tao" and discovery of the archetype of the Self. (MDR, p. 207, 208)

This is an important ecopsychological concept. Each unit, whether human, other living form, or inorganic element is unique and can be lost in a statistical averaging. The tunneling electron microscope has shown there is greater uniqueness in different samples of a particular compound than there are similarities. Relationships are important, but at their best they are relationships between clearly defined individuals. A person is assisted in developing a sense of uniqueness by relating to others and noticing how they both resemble and are different from others. There is strength in diversity—if individuals are developed *and their relationships* are properly dealt with. "Individual" and "culture" are relative concepts: "What is the sound of one hand clapping?" The symbolic dynamics of the process of the development of the individual and its relationship to others will be explored in the volume 3 on Hermes.

Freud dismissed *Psychological Types* as "the work of a snob and a mystic, no new idea in it," objecting to Jung's insistence that there could be no "objective truth" in psychology because of "personal differences in the observer's constitution," now called typological differences. (Bair 2003, p. 286) (n 59) Nonetheless, in 1921 at age 46 Jung was considered to be Freud's only worthy theoretical rival with his emphasis on "the whole man." (Bair 2003, p. 288, 289) His intense "scientific work" demonstrated the existence of archetypal themes. (n 60) Jung's deep personal experience revealed common themes of all humankind, thereby reconnecting him to the rest of humanity.

After developing the concept of the Self, Jung was able to find his way back to the world by lecturing, traveling and writing, activities that "formed a kind of counterpoise to the years of interior searching." (MDR, p. 208) (n 61) Not until 1927 at age 52 when he had his Liverpool dream with its revelation of the Self was he satisfied with his analytic system of psychology. He was to spend 45 years trying to understand what emerged in his confrontation with the unconscious:

> The years when I was pursuing my inner images were the most important in my life—in them everything essential was decided. It all began then; the later details are only supplements and clarifications of the material that burst forth from the unconscious, and at first swamped me. It was the *prima materia* for a lifetime's work. (p. 199) (n 62)

CHAPTER 8

Alchemy, "The Light of Nature," and the Post-Christian Unconscious

It took about 20 years after the "confrontation" before Jung could say "I reached some degree of understanding of my fantasies" by finding historical and literary parallels to substantiate his personal experience. (MDR, p. 200) He began with a cursory study of the cabala and a more detailed look at Gnosticism because Philemon had a Gnostic flavor. Like Philemon, "the practitioners of this early Christian sect…possessed esoteric knowledge of spiritual things" but Jung could not unearth enough information to understand their concept of the Godhead. (Bair 2003, p. 396) (n 63) Dreams helped lead Jung to his "momentous discovery" of alchemy, which he began to study seriously around 1930-31. (n 64) No writers had touched upon "the dark substance…the dark side" of a God that could defecate on his church. Jung began to fixate on a dream he had during his student years that he hoped alchemy would help him sort out. Jung felt very insecure during those years, and wished for "a direct experience of the eternal, of a sighting of God." He then dreamt he would finally have this experience if he opened a door. "I opened this door and what was behind it—a big manure heap and on top of it there lay a big sow"—an experience almost as bad as God defecating on the Basel Cathedral. (p. 397)

The pig is one of *the* archetypal images of the feminine, particularly in her nourishing and nurturing roles as the Great Mother. (Bair 2003, p. 660 note 45) Anyone witnessing a sow lying on her side with a host of sucking piglets knows what this archetype is about. Yet the sow in Jung's dream was atop a manure pile presumably of its own making or at least associated with waste, smell and rejected material. Jung's childhood experience of his mother abandoning him during her hospitalizations and her bizarre and hysterical nature led Jung to fear her and possibly develop a lifelong mistrust of women. (p. 657 note 11) Jung associated women "naturally" with the Eros function and men with Logos. (p. 394) Scientific research beginning with Harry Harlow's monkeys-and-love experiments, psychoanalytic research, and human developmental studies have demonstrated the connection between poor infant-mother bonding and deep narcissistic wounds that affect one's ability to form long-lasting, intimate relationships. Attachment theorists like Daniel Siegel (1999) have fully developed this theme, which clearly reflects Jung's experience. To further complicate the situation, Jung's homosexual abuse, probably in his teen-age years with a Catholic priest and friend of his father, crippled his ability to form intimate relationships with men. (Bair 2003, p. 71, 72, 281-283) (n 65) It may have affected his connection with his body and sexuality. See Appendix G: Jung's Eros Wound and his Image of God.

At the archetypal cultural level the dream refers to the repressed feminine in Western culture. This is illustrated by our difficult relationship with Eros and the Judeo-Christian suppression of the erotic Mother goddess cults of the ancient Middle East. (see volume 3, Appendix G: The Sacred Prostitute and the Erotic Feminine and Appendix H: The Black Goddess) (n 66)

Jung said he "had stumbled upon the historical counterpart of my psychology of the unconscious " with his discovery of alchemy. (MDR, p. 205) It gave substance to his psychology and an understanding of unconscious contents from a historical perspective and collective material. Here was a symbolic system within which to frame his "confrontation with the unconscious" and develop his theoretical system. He began to focus his attention on the nature of the archetype, believing that working with neuroses and dreams required a knowledge of the archetypes, the transpersonal "historical dominants" that shape a culture through their affect on individual lives. (p. 205, 206) (n 67) This is most easily seen in Westerner's attitudes towards the feminine, sex, sensuality, aggression, and nature.

Alchemy, "grounded in the natural philosophy of the Middle Ages," provided the historical link of the contemporary world with Gnosticism as an early Christian sect and the revival of neo-Platonism during the Renaissance. (MDR, p. 201) (see volume 3, Appendix K: Archetypal Psychology and Aphrodite as the Soul of the World) Gnostics believed a higher god gave humankind a *krater* (mixing vessel), a feminine principle and the vessel of spiritual transformation. (p. 201) It is "a kind of uterus of spiritual renewal and rebirth, and corresponded to the alchemical vas in which the transformation of substances took place." (p. 201 note 1) (n 68)

Alchemy also linked Jung's experiences with the "light of nature," considered since the Middle Ages to be a second source of knowledge along with Christian revelation. (von Franz 1975, p. 31) (n 69) Revelation is believed to be knowledge received directly from God and not knowledge about God obtained through the study of God as It manifests in nature. Jung committed himself to the "light of nature" and as an empirical natural scientist was convinced "that the facts of nature are the basis of all knowledge." (p. 32) Nature is not only without but also within. Von Franz writes, "The collective human psyche is a piece of nature...an objective Something that is not 'made' by our subjective ego but which it confronts as an objective other" (p. 33):

> So at the source of the dream there is a creative mystery which we cannot rationally explain. It's the creativity of nature. It's the same creativity which has created what man could never invent: the millions of species of animals and flowers and plants on the earth. The dreams are also like flowers or plants. They are something unique which we can only marvel at. (Unknown source)

Goethe's *Faust* was Jung's first encounter with the light of nature presented in an alchemical format. Jung experienced an inner relationship to Goethe through his study of alchemy. (n 70) Jung said his Personality No. 2 felt "in secret accord with the Middle Ages, as personified by Faust." (MDR, p. 87) He could see a connection between Mephistopheles and his Personality No. 2 manifesting in the phallus dream, the little black manikin, and the luminous radiolarian dream. (von Franz 1975, p. 33, 34) Alchemical studies helped Jung realize that Mephistopheles did not personify the Christian devil but was rather a parallel of the alchemical Mercurius,

> that "godlike companion" of the lonely adept who reveals to him the mysteries of nature. Mephistopheles initiates the intellectual, weary scholar Faust into the world of Eros and leads him...into the depths...down to the Mothers and the mystery of the "god in nature." (p. 34)

Jung's initial response to alchemy was that it was total nonsense. Eventually he realized the alchemists were speaking symbolically, and he devoted almost a decade of study to delineate the symbolic base and archetypal themes of alchemy. (MDR, p. 204, 205) He appreciated alchemy for being close to the unconscious with a smell and feel of its raw material before it got worked over and refined into myths, great art and religious practices. He revered alchemy as a symbolic representation of the basic processes of deep psychic transformation. Alchemy helped Jung develop the central concept of his analytic approach, the process of individuation. Through alchemy he realized that the unconscious is a process that "undergoes or produces change" and "the psyche is transformed or developed by the relationship of the ego to the contents of the unconscious." (p. 209)

Jung eventually plumbed the depths of alchemy, which he said brought his psychological system to its "outermost border," forcing him to recognize "the transcendent, about which nothing can be said." (Bair 2003, p. 398) Von Franz, Jung's closest compatriot who did much of the groundwork for Jung's alchemical studies, related Jung's life work to his study of alchemy:

> The basis and substance of Jung's entire life and work do not lie in the traditions and religions which have become contents of collective consciousness, but rather in that primordial experience which is the final source of these contents: the encounter of the single individual with his own god or daimon, his struggle with the overpowering emotions, affects, fantasies and creative inspirations and obstacles which come to light from within. (von Franz 1975, p. 13, 14)

At the collective level the transformations depicted in alchemy are seen in the development and evolution of religions and their changing symbols. (MDR, p. 209) Spiritual experiences bring about changes in perspectives, values and behavior, thereby changing a culture. When the Self manifests and captures a person like Jesus, there is a dynamism and emotional fullness in that individual and in their followers. As centuries pass, the experience becomes part of collective consciousness and is gradually reduced to empty dogmas and rituals. A conflict develops between knowledge/experience and belief/faith. (CW 8, ¶ 426; von Franz 1975, 178-184) Jung said Protestantism suffers from a significant loss of "the richness of Catholic ceremony and ritual," contributing to an indescribable sense of emptiness and longing. (Bair 2003, p. 474)

Jung identified "*the* social pathology of modernity" as being the prominence of the "mass man" of the collective consciousness and the failure of religion to form an adequate counterweight. (Shamdasani 2003, p. 339, 340) Socio-political movements were inevitably opposed to religion, Jung asserted, as the religious attitude maintained that the individual is ultimately dependent on higher powers. It is above all the religions that have always spoken to man's No. 2, to the "inner man" (p. 39, note 2), but the State has come to take the place of God. Organized religions have been of little help in countering this, as they too seem to favor collective action. (CW 10, ¶ 511, 515, 516, 536) (n 72) Jung saw his system of analytical psychology with its emphasis on the collective unconscious and individuation as the "only solution...which could save the West from catastrophe." (Shamdasani 2003, p. 339, 340) The experience of the Self in the individuation process establishes an inner spiritual authority in counter position to mass psychology and "Caesar's world." (MDR, 211, 212) (see Appendix C: The Anthropos) Jung considered his approach to be part of the emerging astrological "Age of Aquarius," a "New Age," two terms he coined. (Jung 1973, p. 285; Bair 2003, p. 471)

Jung felt it was his fate and obligation "to bring my knowledge of the unconscious into the reality of our spiritual tradition" (Bair 2003, p. 398), believing, as Shamdasani stated it, that his psychology would "enable the reformulation of the humanities and revitalize religions." (Shamdasani 2003, p. 15) Jung explored the relationship between psychology and religion and its affect on one's worldview in "Psychology and Religion." (CW 11, p. 3-105) The fundamental problem in many of his patients, he believed, was their meaningless lives with too narrow a spiritual horizon. Caught up in the things of the world—work, reputation, marriage—they often lose their faith. Many could deeply connect with their religions if they could live its symbolic dimensions, but most lacked the vital participation with symbols necessary for that to happen. (MDR, p. 140)

Alchemy helped Jung see Christianity in a new light. He considered Christianity to be of central importance to the West but believed it needs "to be seen in a new light, in accordance with the changes wrought by the contemporary spirit. Otherwise, it stands apart from the times, and has no effect on man's wholeness." (MDR, p. 210) Humans are co-creators of the universe with the Self, and as consciousness evolves, the relationship with the Self must evolve or religion mortifies.

One aspect of Jung's attempt to revitalize Christianity involved Gnosticism, which put an emphasis on sexuality and sought to unite Christianity with the nature religions. (see Appendix H: The Black Goddess in volume 3) Amfortas of the Grail legend, popular in Medieval Europe, had a wound in the groin, in his sexual nature. (see Appendix D: Merlin and the Grail Legend) Jung experienced the underground god—sexuality—God's dark chthonic brother, in his childhood nightmare. He spoke in Parts V and VI of *The Seven Sermons* of sexuality and spirituality as being powerful daemons, manifestations of the gods, which reveal the world of the gods. (MDR, p. 386-389) They reach beyond human nature, "existing in themselves," possessing and containing us and not vice versa. It is our "common task and danger, a common burden" for humans to stand under the laws of spirituality and sexuality and distinguish ourselves from them. (p. 387)

The Catholic church and many conservative Protestant groups encourage sexuality for reproduction but repress sexuality in association with the god Eros, relationship. (see Appendix H: The Black Goddess and Appendix G: The Sacred Prostitute and the Erotic Feminine in volume 3) A consequence is overpopulation "which Jung regarded as a greater danger to mankind in the long run than even the atom bomb." Sixties style "free love" sexuality is mostly carnal sexuality that often had little to do with relationship and Eros. (Hannah 1991, p. 152)

Alchemy as a form of religious philosophy addressed the lack of wholeness in Christianity (see CW 12, *Psychology and Alchemy* published in 1944). Christ is an incomplete and unsatisfying symbol of the Self for many contemporary people because he does not contain the archetypes of the anima and animus and particularly lacks the dark side, the shadow, and sexuality. The official Christ image expressed in the Protestant Western church of Jung's time had evolved into something that was too spiritual, rarefied and remote from the human heart. (CW 13, ¶ 127) Christ became too much associated with the all-good and all-light, with the Christian focus on a transcendent realm and an after life. The emphasis on light and a perfect Christ was necessary to broaden and intensify consciousness in the early era of Christianity, "but this led in the course of time to a split and to an almost unbearable moral conflict in man." (von Franz 1975, p. 231, 232) Jung felt it was his task to answer the questions of his representative Christian parents and ancestors concerning essential problems with Christianity. (MDR, p. 214, 215, 233, 234)

Through their *opus* the alchemists experienced a fundamental transformation of the official Christian image of God and man by incorporating the feminine and the light of nature to achieve a new fullness and completeness. Jung was profoundly shaken in 1939 by an "essentially alchemical vision of Christ." (MDR, p. 211) He awoke one night to a vision of a greenish-gold Christ on the cross bathed in bright light at the foot of his bed. Jung realized an analogy was being made between Christ and the "green spirit" of the alchemists, the life spirit that animates the entire universe—man, nature, and the inorganic realm:

> My vision was thus a union of the Christ-image with his analogue in matter, the *filius macrocosmi* [son of the macrocosm]...[It was an] undisguised alchemical conception of Christ as a union of spiritually alive and physically dead matter. (p. 211)

54

CHAPTER 9

Bollingen—an Architectural Alchemical Vessel

To understand the essence of Jung and his lived relationship with nature and alchemy, one has to appreciate the retreat he built at Bollingen. There Jung felt closest to his true self and had a palpable sense of the "two million-year-old man within"—the archetypal level in humans that is in and is part of nature. Bollingen was "a kind of representation in stone of my innermost thoughts and of the knowledge I had acquired...[It is] a confession of faith in stone." (MDR, p. 223) He knew from the start he had to build near water, a thought that became fixed in his mind after experiencing "inconceivable pleasure" at being beside a lake as a very young child. (p. 7) In 1922, at age 47, he bought land on Lower Lake Zurich with the thought of building "a kind of primitive one-story dwelling." He had in mind a type of round African hut with a fire in the middle around which family life revolved: "Primitive huts concretize an idea of wholeness, a familial wholeness in which all sorts of small domestic animals likewise participate." (p. 223, 224) This seemed too primitive, so he altered it into a two-story house that became a suitable dwelling tower in 1923:

> The feeling of repose and renewal that I had in this Tower was intense from the start. It represented for me the maternal hearth. (p. 224)

> From the beginning I felt the Tower as in some way a place of maturation—a maternal womb or a maternal figure in which I could become what I was, what I am and will be. It gave me a feeling as if I were being reborn in stone. It is thus a concretization of the individuation process. (p. 225)

Tower construction began two months after his mother's death. Given his childhood attachment problems with his mother and his nighttime fears of her, one could see the tower as a concrete expression of a positive mother symbol within which Jung could be contained and nurtured. The powerful association of his mother's No. 2 personality with nature and the deep primal nature of Jung's attachment wound may have been behind his initial attraction to a primitive and circular design for the tower. Note also that animals living within the family confines were an important aspect of wholeness in Jung's imagination.

A central structure with a tower-like annex was added four years later and the annex was extended four years after that, becoming a place of spiritual concentration. Only Jung had the key to that room where he said, "I could exist for myself alone." (see Jung's tower fantasy in his mid-teens, p. 12). Over the years he did paintings on the walls and added sayings with pictorial representations, "and so have expressed all those things which have carried me out of time into seclusion, out of the present into timelessness." (MDR, p. 224)

After another four years, in 1935, he added a courtyard and a loggia by the lake. Open to the sky and to nature, the larger space completed a quaternity of four-year cycles of building. He finished building after his wife's death in 1955 when he was 77, realizing that all the parts fit together to form a symbol of psychic wholeness. Jung had an important insight:

> I suddenly realized that the small central section which crouched so low, so hidden, was myself! I could no longer hide myself behind the "maternal" and the "spiritual" towers. So, in that same year, I added an upper story to this section, which represents myself, or my ego-personality... It signified an extension of consciousness achieved in old age. (MDR, p. 225)

Emma as mother and nurturing anima was represented by the original tower with its combined kitchen and bedroom, and Toni was represented by the second tower—a "self-containedly spiritual" place. With the last addition Jung said he could "start emphasizing myself now" and "overcome the feeling of 'disappear[ing] between the two towers.'" Jung called this last construction "the chapel," and it gave him "a sort of a strange rapture" to be in the room. "It was also supposed to be a sort of a grave," he said, that reminded him of a sacred crypt he visited as a student that "displaced [him]...from the world, into the nontemporal, into eternity." (Bair 2003, p. 324)

Jung had developed Bollingen into an architectural alchemical vessel, a place where his deepest thoughts and transformations could occur. It took him 77 years, most of them engaged in intense self-analysis and the development of consciousness, before he felt he could manifest to the world the strong and whole ego personality he had become.

Jung had many powerful experiences at Bollingen, beginning with his first week alone in the original tower. While boiling water in a kettle, he was fascinated by a sound "like many voices...or...even like a whole orchestra" making soft polyphonic music that exchanged dominance with the wind orchestra blowing outside the tower:

> For far more than an hour I listened to the concert, to this natural melody. It was soft music, containing, as well, all the discords of nature...For nature is not only harmonious; she is also dreadfully contradictory and chaotic. The music was that way too: an outpouring of sounds, having the quality of water and of wind—so strange that it is simply impossible to describe it. (MDR, p. 229)

He spent about half his time at Bollingen, usually alone. (Bair 2003, p. 768 note 36) Barbara Hannah felt a special quality about the place, perhaps because it had been old church land: "You feel far more in yourself there than elsewhere and after any illness it has a singularly healing quality." (Hannah 1991, p. 154) Jung wrote:

> At Bollingen I am in the midst of my true life, I am most deeply myself. Here I am, as it were, the "age-old son of the mother." That is how alchemy puts it, very wisely, for the "old man," the "ancient," whom I had already experienced as a child, is Personality No. 2, who has always been and always will be. He exists outside time and is the son of the maternal unconscious. In my fantasies he took the form of Philemon, and he comes to life again at Bollingen.

> At times I feel as if I am spread out over the landscape and inside things, and am myself living in every tree, in the splashing of the waves, in the clouds and the animals that come and go, in the procession of the seasons. There is nothing in the Tower that has not grown into its own form over the decades, nothing with which I am not linked. Here everything has its history, and mine; here is space for the spaceless kingdom of the world's and the psyche's hinterland.

> I have done without electricity, and tend the fireplace and stove myself. Evenings, I light the old lamps. There is no running water, and I pump the water from the well. I chop

the wood and cook the food. These simple acts make man simple; and how difficult it is to be simple!

In Bollingen, silence surrounds me almost audibly, and I live "in modest harmony with nature." Thoughts rise to the surface which reach back into the centuries, and accordingly anticipate a remote future. Here the torment of creation is lessened; creativity and play are close together. (MDR, p. 225, 226)

Hannah noted that Jung's No. 2 personality, "that timeless or eternal figure in man," was entirely constellated at Bollingen, where Jung wore old clothes suited for simple physical tasks (Hannah 1991, p. 155):

When he first got there from the outside world, he always spent some days acclimatizing himself to the place, doing all those jobs that have to be done in the simple life there or even just staring at the lake. Then, when he was thoroughly in tune with the world of No. 2, his best ideas came to him, and he wrote as No. 2 wished, although of course No. 1 did the actual writing, translating ideas too strange into language that could be understood...The most creative part [of his writing] was always done at Bollingen. (p. 155, 156)

One of Jung's favorite occupations was chopping wood. (Hannah 1991, p. 323) He was an unusually good cook and would get entirely engrossed in cooking or watching the fire, during which time many ideas came to him. (p. 199) Spending hours building little waterworks—dams and diversions—on a tiny stream that ran through his property also was a mind-clearing and idea-generating pastime. (Jaffe 1979, p. 196, 197)

On the premises he dedicated a phallic cornerstone to Atis who symbolized the eternal spring-like glory of life. (Attis was the son-lover of the love and fertility goddess Cybele. See Appendix G: The Sacred Prostitute and the Erotic Feminine in volume 3) Attis linked back to his childhood nightmare and the archetypal base of his life. (von Franz 1975, p. 23) In 1950, at age 75, Jung made a kind of monument out of stone in the courtyard to express what the tower meant to him. He had rescued a cubic cornerstone that had been delivered with the wrong dimensions and was about to be sent back. Jung chiseled images and statements into it, beginning with a dictum about the alchemical stone that was despised and rejected by fools but "loved by the wise." Into another side of the stone he carved a figure of a hooded child carrying a lantern—a kind of Kabir or Telesphoros of Asklepios with phallic symbolism. (see Appendix H: Jung's Phallic Self Image) He roams the cosmos and "glows like a star out of the depths. He points the way to the gates of the sun and to the land of dreams." On the third face he chiseled quotations from alchemy about an orphan found everywhere who is young and old at the same time, without parents but fetched out of the deep like a fish, roams woods and mountains but remains hidden in the innermost soul of man, mortal to everyone but "not touched by the cycle of aeons." (MDR, p. 227)

Jung wanted to chisel *"Le cri de Merlin!"* into the back face of the stone:

> For what the stone expressed reminded me of Merlin's life in the forest, after he had vanished from the world. Men still hear his cries, so the legend runs, but they cannot understand or interpret them.
>
> Merlin represents an attempt by the medieval unconscious to create a parallel figure to Parsifal. Parsifal is a Christian hero [the "innocent" who found the Holy Grail], and Merlin, son of the devil and a pure virgin, is his dark brother. In the twelfth century, when the legend arose, there were as yet no premises by which his intrinsic meaning could be understood. Hence he ended in exile, and hence *"le cri de Merlin"* which still sounded from the forest after his death. This cry that no one could understand implies that he lives on in unredeemed form. His story is not yet finished, and he still walks abroad. It might be said that the secret of Merlin was carried on by alchemy, primarily in the figure of Mercurius [god of the alchemists]. Then Merlin was taken up again in my psychology of the unconscious and—remains uncomprehended to this day! That is because most people find it quite beyond them to live on close terms with the unconscious. Again and again I have had to learn how hard this is for people. (MDR, p. 228)

Jung felt Merlin was "the great tragic figure in this whole epic" and infinitely "more important than Parsifal" because "he represents the actual solution of the problem of opposites." He was a magician but "not really evil." Jung wrote, "Something inside me always identified with that figure [i.e., the combination of Merlin/Parsifal]," and added, "Merlin disappears in the woods—He goes to Bollingen!" (Bair 2003, p. 758 note 64) (see Appendix D: Merlin and the Grail Legend)

Since Jung could more easily enter the archetypal realm at Bollingen, it is not surprising there were many associations of the Tower with ancestors and the realm of the dead. As mentioned, he began construction just after his mother died and completed it after his wife's death. When Jung's eldest and psychic daughter first visited Bollingen in 1923 she exclaimed: "there are corpses about!" Four years later they discovered a skeleton 7 feet underground. (MDR, p. 231) After Emma died in 1955 after 52 years of marriage, Jung spent months chiseling the names of his paternal ancestors on stone tablets before placing them in the courtyard of the Tower. He painted a ceiling at Bollingen with motifs from the familial coats of arms. The revised Jung family coat of arms contained alchemical imagery that symbolized the union of Christian and Dionysian elements, the heavenly and chthonic spirits. (MDR, p. 232) (n 73) While working on the stone tablets, Jung became aware of the "fateful links between me and my ancestors. I feel very strongly that I am under the influence of things or questions which were left incomplete and unanswered by my parents and grandparents and more distant ancestors." (p. 233) He had long felt it was his fate to answer Christianity's unanswered questions about the origin of evil and the lack of the sacred feminine, the Dionysian side of life, and the issues around the "restless Wotan-Hermes of my Alemannic and Frankish ancestors." (p. 318) If archetypal, collective problems in society are not recognized, he was sure they caused personal disturbances in the psyche whose roots are not of a personal nature. (p. 233, 234)

Jung carved over a doorway at Bollingen the same statement in Latin he had carved over the front door of his Kusnacht home: "Whether called or not, God will be present" (an adage of Erasmus). The saying reminded Jung that "the true beginning of wisdom lay in fear and awe of God." (Bair 2003, p. 126; Psalms 111: 10) For Jung, "God was a certainty as well as a mystery." (p. 127; Jung 1976a, p. 383, 384)

Jung felt compelled to carve a memorial at Bollingen to Goethe's *Faust*, feeling such a deep and intimate connection to this writing that all the crises of the drama affected him personally. (n 74) "Goethe had written virtually a basic outline and pattern of my own conflicts and solutions. The dichotomy of Faust-Mephistopheles came together within myself into a single person, and I was that person." (MDR, p. 235) For Jung, *Faust* was the pure expression of a collective German experience that anticipated the people's political fate. He believed the heroic archetype stirred up by Wagner and "the Dionysian experience of Nietzsche—which might better be ascribed to the god of ecstasy,

Wotan," were collective factors leading to the German engagement in World War I. (MDR, p. 234, 235; also see CW 10, ¶ 371-487)

Jung thought Mephistopheles was much closer to Mercurius than the Christian Devil. He was disposed of and relegated to hell with a cheap trick by the angels:

> Faust's fate shows what happens when the constellated archetypal images of Mercurius meets a weak and morally childish consciousness which cannot defend its ethical integrity; he seduced it into betrayal and murder. For Faust—in order to wrest more land from the sea—disposed of that old couple, Philemon and Baucis, who, according to legend, were the only ones still worshipping the gods Jupiter and Mercury [Hermes] in a time of general decay and immorality. (von Franz 1975, p. 212, 213)

Von Franz, writing in 1975, adds that Faust's inflation compares with "the arrogant, hubris-filled way in which we are today destroying the natural environment and whose evil consequences we are just beginning to recognize." (p. 213)

Since first reading *Faust* at age 16, Jung believed that the ending should be different. (Bair 2003, p. 399) Goethe had mentioned Philemon "only in passing" whereas Jung thought he was a "central figure... a recognition that Faust skipped over and didn't achieve." (p. 398, 399) Philemon ("=Kiss") was "the complete opposite to the Superman Faust, the product of the devil." (p. 757 note 48) Because of his identity with *Faust*, Jung personally felt it necessary to atone for the murder of Philemon: he carved a Latin inscription over the gate of his Bollingen tower translated as "Shrine of Philemon—Repentance of Faust." (MDR, p. 235 note 5) He saw his life's work as "consciously link[ing] my work to what Faust had passed over: respect for the eternal rights of man [individuation], recognition of 'the ancient' [the collective unconscious] and the continuity of culture and intellectual history [archetypes and the cultural unconscious]." (p. 235)

Jung summarized his experience at Bollingen by commenting on our psychic inheritance and its relationship to modern science and technology. He advocated a simple life style outside a consumer-oriented society, a life style that valued the inner life and was close to nature:

> We are very far from having finished completely with the Middle Ages [when alchemy and the Grail legend arose], classical antiquity [the Greeks and Romans], and primitiv-

ity ["the two million-year-old man within"], as our modern psyches pretend. Nevertheless, we have plunged down a cataract of progress which sweeps us on into the future with ever wilder violence the farther it takes us from our roots... We live more in the future and its chimerical promises of a golden age than in the present...We rush impetuously into novelty, driven by a mounting sense of insufficiency, dissatisfaction, and restlessness. (MDR, p. 236)

Inner peace and contentment depend in large measure upon whether or not the historical family which is inherent in the individual can be harmonized with the ephemeral conditions of the present. (p. 237)

Jung came to these realizations most easily at Bollingen, his concretized symbol of wholeness that connected him to the ancestors and the land:

In the Tower at Bollingen it is as if one lived in many centuries simultaneously...There is nothing to disturb the dead, neither electric light nor telephone. Moreover, my ancestors' souls are sustained by the atmosphere of the house, since I answer for them the questions that their lives once left behind...It is as if a silent, greater family, stretching down the centuries, were peopling the house. There I live in my second personality and see life in the round, as something forever coming into being and passing on. (MDR, p. 237)

CHAPTER 10

Looking at Europe from Outside:
Travels to Africa and America

Jung traveled extensively in a determined attempt to get an objective view of European culture by looking at it from the outside. He made the rather surprising statement that his study of the psychic life of non-Europeans, beginning with North Africa and Taos, New Mexico, offered the first clues to an adequate explanation of his experiences between 1913-1917. (Jung and Jaffe, p. 356 referenced in Shamdasani 2003, p. 322) His first trip to a totally foreign country was to Tunis in North Africa in 1924. He felt like he had journeyed back through centuries of time when he visited a desert oasis. He was deeply moved and more disturbed than he realized by the highly emotional nature of the Muslim Arabs, believing them to have marginal reflective abilities. This was a cultural bias of early 20th century Europeans and a thesis popular in Europe at the end of the 19th century. "Phylogenetic inheritance" proposed that less civilized cultures corresponded "in some manner to phylogenetic layers in the unconscious of Europeans." (Shamdasani 2005, p. 106) The theory equated primitive culture with a childlike state of consciousness, the dream state, and deeper layers of the modern psyche; therefore studying primitive cultures would be a way of learning more about these three areas, and vice versa. (see Appendix B: The Animal Soul, the Primordial Mind and Archetypes in volume 1)

Jung saw in "primitive" peoples a childlike state of consciousness, more naïve than Europeans, but also more complete and whole because less culturally formed and less ego-driven. He believed this quality of wholeness, combined with their emotional vitality, created a powerful unconscious attraction to the highly rational and culturally adapted European. This put Europeans in danger of "going black under the skin" when immersed in "primitive" cultures (MDR, p. 244-246) and indicates the magnitude of Jung's challenge to Westerners to integrate our cultured side with the indigenous one within.

Jung got a warning about "going black" on his last night in Tunis. He dreamt he was being drowned by a dark Arab prince appearing as a dark Self figure—the dark side of God. (MDR, p. 242-244) Reflecting and grappling with his cultural biases, Jung can be seen as an exemplar of the collective unconscious of the Western Judeo-Christian traditions wrestling with suppressed emotional states. These states are associated with the ancient love goddess cults (see Appendix G: The Sacred Prostitute and the Erotic Feminine and Appendix H: The Black Goddess in volume 3), energies related to the emotionality of "the Dionysian side of life." This aspect appears in blind Salome who Jung met with Elijah on his first descent into the unconscious. (p. 181, 182) What Jung, and by extension European culture, needed to experience and integrate into consciousness was the relatedness and emotional vitality of Eros. (p. 244-246)

Jung detected a strong emotional nature in the Muslim religion, with God really being a call; the call to prayer evokes a deep, inarticulable emotional response. When he heard the call "Allah" echoing through the hall of a Cairo mosque he had the "feeling that the call itself penetrated to heaven." (Hannah 1991, p. 180) By contrast to the archetypal Eros of feminine relatedness in the Muslim religion (p. 143, 144), Jung saw Christianity and the other great religions as being founded on Logos, the masculine principle of discrimination. (p. 143) Logos is the god of form experienced as a revelation and not as logical or intellectual thinking. John's gospel equates Christ with Logos: "In the beginning was the Word." (p. 144) (n 75)

Jung's second cultural venture was a visit to a Taos pueblo in New Mexico in 1925, where he came to a better understanding of the "indigenous one within." He formed an immediate connection with the Taos chief Mountain Lake and considered the conversations with him to be some of the key conversations in his life. (Shamdasani 2005, p. 106) "I talked to him sympathetically as if he were a patient in advanced analysis," Jung said. (19 January 1925, Baynes papers quoted in Shamdasani 2005, p. 107) Jung had "the extraordinary sensation that I was talking to an Egyptian priest of the fifteenth century before Christ." (16 January 1925, Dodge Papers, Beineke library in Shamdasani 2005, p. 106) Mountain Lake thought whites looked cruel and were always seeking and wanting something, always uneasy and restless. He did not understand whites, thinking them all to be mad because they thought with their heads, while Indians thought with their hearts. (MDR, p. 248) (see James Hillman's *The Thought of the Heart and The Soul of the*

World 1992 and Appendix K in volume 3) For the first time in his life, Jung got a picture of "the real white man":

> What we from our point of view call colonization, missions to the heathen, spread of civilization, etc., has another face—the face of a bird of prey seeking with cruel intentness for distant quarry—a face worthy of a race of pirates and highwaymen. All the eagles and other predatory creatures that adorn our coats of arms seem to me apt psychological representatives of our true nature. (p. 248, 249)

Jung was impressed by the absolute inaccessibility of the Indian religion. He discouraged anthropologists from probing the mysteries of the Pueblo religion, believing that gave them a sense of pride and cohesion and the ability to resist domination by white culture. (MDR, p. 249, 250) The Indians showed "surprising emotion," often with tears in their eyes, when speaking of things pertaining to the mysteries. (p. 250) Mountain Lake told Jung that his people were sons of the Father Sun. Living at the roof of the world, their religion helped the sun rise every day—something the whole world depended on. (p. 251, 252) Jung wrote, "That [man] can render back something which is essential even to God, induces pride, for it raises the human individual to the dignity of a metaphysical factor." This gave the Pueblo a sense of serenity: "Such a man is in the fullest sense of the word in his proper place." (p. 253) (n 76)

Sonu Shamdasani summarily stated the importance of anthropology to a Jungian ecopsychology:

> The task for the modern [is] one of regaining this mythic and cosmological embeddedness exemplified by the Pueblos, without sacrificing the gains of modern consciousness. Individuation was conceived [by Jung] as a conjunction which resolved the conflict between the primitive and the modern.
>
> Neurosis was conceived as consisting in a conflict between the primitive and the modern. Not only did he claim that primitive mentality survived in the unconscious, he equated the two. Anthropology could be put to a new use—to provide knowledge of the modern unconscious. In a seminar, in 1923, he noted that the understanding of primitive mentality was essential for the analysis of dreams. (Shamdasani 2003, p. 328) (n 77)

Jung believed the shadow of Americans was much bigger than Europeans because Americans had fairly recently left their European roots and crossed the Atlantic. Because Europeans had been settled on their own soil for many centuries, they find a shadow of their own race when they enter the unconscious, but Americans come up against an Indian or Negro shadow. Americans have "Negro behavior and an Indian soul" according to Jung. "Everywhere the virgin earth causes at least the unconscious of the conqueror to sink to the level of its indigenous inhabitants." (n 78) Because the gap between American consciousness and the shadow is so large it generates more psychic energy than a European, giving them "an indomitable spirit of enterprise and an enviable enthusiasm." (CW 10, ¶ 103)

Jung noted the "extraordinarily strong influence" of African Americans on white American behavior—the laugh, loose limbs and swinging hips, the strong black influence on purely American music and dance, the emotional religious revivals, a certain naiveté—"both charming and less acceptable"—and a "boundless sociability and social life" not unlike an African village. (Hannah 1991, p. 163, 164)

Jung got the full experience of primitive culture by taking a journey of several months into the heart of Africa in 1925. He traveled with three comrades by train and by foot through Kenya and Uganda, then took a long, dangerous hike north to catch a boat up the Nile. Upon returning from the trip to Africa he said:

> It seemed to me that our conventional modes of conceiving and dealing with psychological problems were as inadequate as would be an attempt to use diamonds as road fill...My modern self-assurance suffered a staggering defeat. (Shamdasani 2003, p. 323)

Jung believed anthropologists should study an alien culture by letting themselves be affected by the experience and then reflect objectively on what it does to them. (Shamdasani 2003, p. 324) (n 79) He said he felt "an unconscious identity with everyone" (Bair 2003, p. 349) along with a feeling of unity with all things African (p. 350), adding that he would have to be an artist to convey the depth of emotion he felt. (p. 348)

His "first encounter with the original timeless primitive" was the sight of a lone black hunter gazing down at his train from a cliff in Kenya (Bair 2003, p. 348): "I was enchanted by this sight...I had the feeling that I had already experienced this moment and had always known this world which was separated from me only by distance in time." (MDR, p. 254) That feeling tone lingered throughout his months in Africa: "I enjoyed the 'divine peace' of a still primeval country. Never had I seen so clearly 'man and the other animals' (Herodotus)." (p. 264)

Jung maintained that in Africa and very primitive countries one sees the primeval ancestor and even the animal ancestors on the outside, while in any "confrontation with the unconscious" one meets them on the inside. In both domains one is in the country of the Self, not the ego. (Hannah 1991, p. 172) The outer primitive environment may appear alien to the ego, but one gets a sense of déjà vu because it resonates with, or constellates, the primeval man and animal soul within.

Stated in dynamic systems theory terms, being in a primitive environment facilitates the emergence of the archetypal dimension of human experience; a "just so," always-that-way, eternal sense. It feels like one is experiencing something one has always known and therefore experienced before. Everyone has dreamt of a member of the opposite sex with whom we felt a deep, *eternal* soul-connection. Upon awakening we realize we had never seen such a person.

Jung had a "blissful stay" of almost two months with the Ugandan Elgony of the Masai tribe, getting on so well with the natives they introduced him to the witch doctor, the most powerful member of the tribe. Tearfully he told Jung that medicine men no longer had prognostic dreams: "since the whites were in Africa...Dreams were no longer needed because now the English knew everything!" (MDR, p. 265)

The Elgony shaman told him how the *moment* of the rising sun was associated with God and the principle of light, goodness and beauty. Every morning at sunrise the Elgony spit or blow on their hands, then turn their palms towards the sun, symbolically offering their soul substance to the rising sun. (MDR, p. 266, 267) The sun was not god, but "the *moment* in which the light comes is God" (p. 269), just as God is "the first delicate crescent of the new moon" and not the moon itself. (p. 267) God was a *moment in time*, a process and not a thing. This would link God with the experience of emergence in complexity theory (see Appendices A and B in volume 3) and with Hermes as god of transitions (Appendix E in volume 3).

The Elgony gave equal power and significance to the principle of darkness. It was experienced at night as the breeder of fear, evil and danger. Jung associated these two powers of light and dark with the light and dark acolytes—Horus and Set—of the Egyptian Osiris myth. (MDR, p. 267, 268) He considered the discovery of the Horus principle in the Elgony tribe to be his greatest illumination on the trip. (p. 274) "For untold ages men have worshiped the great god who redeems the world by rising out of the darkness as a radiant light in the heavens." (p. 269) Jung interpreted this as an archetypal human desire for consciousness, for release and redemption from the primordial darkness and maternal mystery of the unconscious: "The myth of Horus is the age-old story of the newly risen divine light...That drama was intimately connected with me, with my psychology." (p. 274) (see Appendix J: Jung's Phallic Self Image)

One must be cautious about Jung's association of pre-historic times with the darkness of unconsciousness. Pre-scientific and pre-historic thinking is a different type of consciousness rather than a greater degree of unconsciousness. Western consciousness is in many ways in the dark about emotions, the body, sexuality and our innate connection with animals and the earth.

Jung believed the Christian sun motif (light of consciousness) came from Egypt where it was the central myth in their religion as the sun God Ra. This realization foreshadowed his discovery of the myth of the birth of consciousness; *the meaning of life [is] what the ego can do for the Self.*" (emphasis added) (Hannah 1991, p. 175) He came to this realization about the cosmic meaning of consciousness while visiting a great game preserve on the Athi Plains of Kenya. While overlooking the massive herds grazing in silence he thought:

> This was the stillness of the eternal beginning, the world as it had always been, in the state of non-being; for until then no one had been present to know that it was this world..." What nature leaves imperfect, the art perfects," say the alchemists. (MDR, p. 255)

Jung discovered his myth of the human's "indispensable place in the great process of being" when he realized that *we* are the second creators of the world because we alone can give it an objective existence. (MDR, p. 255, 256) This objectivity had its mythical beginnings in Genesis when Adam named all the animals. The objectivity of the world was accompanied by a sense of wonder, mystery and beauty for Jung. Norwegian philosopher and founder of deep ecology, Arne Naess, echoes Jung's ecopsychological perspective:

> Essentially there is at present a sorry underestimation of the potentialities of the human species…If it is bound to be anything, perhaps it is to be the conscious joyful appreciator of this planet as an even greater whole of its immense richness. This may be its "evolutionary potential" or an ineradicable part of it. (Naess 1984, p. 8 quoted in Zimmerman 1991, p. 127)

The modern myth is to become aware of, and be dedicated to, continuing the act of creation symbolized by the moment of the rising sun in the Elgony culture. We are to bring the light of consciousness into our dark unconscious substratum and into nature, thereby finding our divine role in creation. (Hannah 1991, p. 175) By this process we raise to consciousness and bring voice, music, image, story, objectivity, symbols, and emotions to the archetypal dynamics and forms that run through the organic and inorganic realms.

Jung felt a strong unity with what he saw as Africa's lonely mood and its "gigantic meaninglessness and endlessly beautiful cruelty. It was as if I had fallen out of any time at all," he said. (Bair 2003, p. 350) But the unconscious sent a warning when he was past the dangerous part of the trip and safely heading home up the Nile. He dreamt of an American Negro barber who had cut his hair in America twelve years earlier: "He was holding a tremendous, red-hot curling iron to my head, intending to make my hair kinky—that is, to give me Negro hair. I could already feel the painful heat, and awoke with a sense of terror." (MDR, p. 272) Jung interpreted the dream as a warning from the unconscious that "the primitive was a danger to me…I was obviously all too close to 'going black'" (MDR, p. 272) and "had been long enough in the blissful peace of the beginning." (Hannah 1991, p. 178) Jung's feeling about the timeless realm of Africa—"God's country" where "inscrutable design" reigned (MDR, p. 256, 257)—and his idea that the primitive mind was like a child with a *participation mystique* in relationship with the world, would connect his African experience with his Personality No. 2 and the timeless realm of the archetypes. The danger he felt from "going black" is an Oedipal warning about getting reabsorbed into the realms of the Mothers rather than taking a conscious position in relation to it. This dream can be linked to the North African dream of an Arab prince as the dark side of the Self who tried to drown him (force him into unconsciousness). (p. 242-246)

CHAPTER 11

A Passage to India

In many ways Jung's most significant journey was his visit to India in 1938 at age 62. It moved him to his core. He wanted to form his own conclusions after he had already "read a great deal about Indian philosophy and religious history, and was deeply convinced of the value of Oriental wisdom" (MDR, p. 274, 275), having collaborated with some of the most important Orientalists of his day. (Shamdasani 2005, p. 109) He was heavily engaged in his study of alchemy at the time, and read one of the principle alchemical texts while on the trip. Jung felt that alchemy and Indian wisdom "both had emerged from original psychic experiences of the unconscious, and therefore had produced the same, similar, or at least comparable insights." (MDR, p. 275)

He was preoccupied with "the psychological nature of evil" while in India (MDR, p. 275), generating seminal thoughts that led to later writings like "Answer to Job." For Easterners, evil is a reality as expressed in the dual nature of their gods. *"Good and evil are meaningfully contained in nature, and are merely varying degrees of the same thing."* (emphasis added) (MDR, p. 276) The mandala is a symbol par excellence for dealing with this tension. Westerners engage in a moral struggle to live the good and overcome the evil, as if it could and should be eliminated. This strengthens the hand of evil which creeps out in Jekyll-and-Hyde fashion. To the Indians, Jung thought, good and evil do not seem to be real or at the most "as *my* good or *my* evil, as whatever seems to me good or evil." They attempt to achieve a position outside good and evil by reaching *nirvana*, a condition of imagelessness and emptiness achieved in meditation or yoga. (p. 276)

Jung gradually came to realize "how far [evil] must be accepted since it is also a part of God's will." (Bair 2003, p. 427) He thought it would be a great mistake however to adopt the Eastern solution of entering nirvana, for it "denies the value of the No. 1 personality," or, in other words, the value of human life in three-dimensional reality. As Jung expressed it:

> I...wish to persist in the state of lively contemplation of nature and of the psychic images. I want to be freed neither from human beings, nor from myself, nor from nature; for all these appear to me the greatest of miracles. Nature, the psyche, and life appear to me like divinity unfolded—and what more could I wish for? To me the supreme meaning of Being can consist only in the fact that it is, not that it is not or is no longer.

> I cannot be liberated from anything that I do not possess, have not done or experienced. Real liberation becomes possible for me only when I have done all that I was able to do, when I have completely devoted myself to a thing and participated in it to the utmost. If I withdraw from participation, I am virtually amputating the corresponding part of my psyche. (MDR, p. 276)

Jung's solution was to develop a mountaintop perspective, like seeing a storm in the valley from a vantage point atop a peak. Developing a broader perspective and seeing things over different time frames (which would include recognition of the consequences of present activities) is an important ecopsychological concept. Metaphorically the storm is like being shaken by the emotional conflicts and torments of life while simultaneously having a mountaintop, higher perspective "which prevents one from total identification with the affect and one can say: 'I *know* that I suffer.'" (CW 13, ¶ 17) Jung felt it is always a defeat to be possessed by a negative emotion and "one was never beyond any human emotion, such as anger or jealousy, but one could always *know* it." (Hannah 1991, p. 282) The development or emergence of a higher or wider perspective helps one see old emotional conflicts in a new light. We are both valley and mountain, for, as Jung said, it is "a vain illusion to deem oneself beyond what is human." (CW 13, ¶ 17) One is not "freed from the general human ills that beset one in the valley" and can "descend into the valley and speak and act in its terms." (Hannah 1991, p. 282) As Barbara Hannah describes it, "we should make every effort to become *conscious* of the eternal [transpersonal, archetypal] standpoint, then do our best to reconcile it with three-dimensional reality in our *actual life*, in the here and now." (p. 266)

The Eastern master Ram Dass said the more he feels the elevated enlightened state (mountain top) achieved by activities like meditation and yoga, the more he can descend into the pain of the world experienced in the heart chakra. At Bollingen Jung was particularly able to achieve the mountaintop perspective. (Hannah 1991, p. 267) If nirvana were not the disappearance of opposites but a meaningful union of opposites as symbolized by the mandala, it would be equivalent to the end stage of alchemy—the second uroborus—and Jung's mountaintop perspective. (see Appendix D: The Alchemy of Psychoanalysis in volume 1)

The Indian imageless and empty state could be thought of as a state of fullness, a pregnant void analogous to pure energy from which any form can arise. A scientific metaphor would be the state before the singularity out of which the universe arose, related to God's command not to make any graven images of the divine because It is the generative source that creates all images and is not to be confined to any image. In Jung's words, it is God as "the most important cause of all things... [who] has no cause." It is synchronicity "as a creative act which comes from the ultimate acausal" (Hannah 1991, p. 307) and Hermes' realm as the transition from non-being into being. (see Appendix E: Hermes as God of Dynamic Systems Theory in volume 3) For Jung, God was not restricted by the dogmas of theologians or the natural "laws" of scientists. In Greek mythology Aphrodite is associated with a fertility that remains virginal, despite intercourse with many gods. Hermes also has a virginal epitaph, related to the psychological importance of the virgin wilderness.

When fully in the moment, divinity is present and God is incarnated; ego and Self are united. After experiencing the *unio mentalis* of alchemy, suffering has meaning and the body is not simply matter but the somatic unconscious with a corporeal spirit—"the stone lighter than air." "Before enlightenment, carry water, chop wood; after enlightenment, carry water, chop wood." Jungian analyst Marion Woodman described this state as being the "conscious feminine"—the manifestation of God in matter as the Goddess, as *Sophia*, the feminine side of God. (Ryley 1998, p. 94) It is experiencing the soul, the soul being "embodied essence," part spirit and part matter. (p. 86) (see Appendix I: The Conscious Feminine) Being in this state can also be described as the difference between being blindly pushed about by emotions and "instinctual drives" at any one moment in a year versus seeing that moment from the broader perspective of the emotional seasons of the entire year—an ecopsychological perspective. Consulting the *I Ching* raises to consciousness what season the soul is in: "For everything there is a season." The personal is transmuted to the eternal when one becomes conscious of the archetypal story one is living. (see Appendix K: Archetypal Psychology and Aphrodite as the Soul of the World in volume 3) This helps make the difficult "personal" experiences bearable and is the beginning of wisdom. In a dynamic systems theory construct, increased intensity of experience will increase the symbolic density of the complex, felt as personal. The system is pushed through a transition phase into the archetypal state (beyond personal and into the impersonal), then perhaps to the Self. (see Appendix B: Bootstrapping the Archetypes in volume 3)

If one is fearful of being overwhelmed by the pain in oneself and/or the world, one may try to avoid engaging reality at all costs. This can become a flight into the spirit as an escape, which Jung did as a child with Personality No. 2. Mark Epstein, M.D., author of *Thoughts Without a Thinker: Psychotherapy from a Buddhist Perspective*, cautions people with deep psychic wounds against using spirituality to "stay above the pit." Doing the pit work becomes part of the spiritual journey the alchemists described. Jungian analyst Ashok Bedi, author of *Path to the Soul*, describes the same problem using the symbolism of the chakra system.

Hexagram 29, "The Abysmal" in the *I Ching*, addressed this issue over 2500 years ago. Taoists used many water metaphors to convey their teachings. The metaphor in "The Abysmal" is of water approaching a pit. It plunges to the bottom and keeps flowing into the pit until it is filled, then the water moves on. It doesn't flow over the top of the pit (repression or suppression of psychologically difficult material or a spiritual escape) nor pile up over the pit once it is full (holding on to a complex). "The Abysmal" is an alchemical metaphor that begins with "the stone that the builders rejected," the lead (what is in the pit) and working with the lead to transmute it into gold. The pit is filled in steps, in quantum leaps of consciousness at the moments of insight when a thought resonates throughout the body. A depth of personality, a wisdom and a richness emerge through this approach. This is the "sweet wound," what Christ means by "Blessed are they that mourn" and "Blessed are the poor in spirit." (see Appendix D: The Alchemy of Psychoanalysis in volume 1 for a therapeutic description of this process)

Barbara Hannah described her experience of the opposites in Jung:

> It is surprising to find a human being in whom [the opposites] exist simultaneously. I felt at one and the same time

> that Jung could be more direct, even ruthless, than anyone
> else I had known—and indeed *he was* when necessary...and
> yet he also obviously had the warmest possible heart and
> a rare love of humanity. You experienced these two quali-
> ties, each made curiously relative by the presence of its also
> fully accepted opposite, *simultaneously* and could take the
> one because of the other. Above all, his geniality and lively
> sense of humor made him completely acceptable, however
> ruthless he chose to be. (Hannah 1991, p. 192)

This description resonates with that of Jesus who was loving but could be ruthlessly harsh, as when throwing the moneychangers out of the temple. He told us "to be as wise as serpents and as innocent as doves" (Matt. 10: 16)—another union of opposites. An abstract expression of the union of opposites is conveyed by the Chinese yin-yang symbol.

Jung was the most whole person Hannah had ever seen, having

> [a] quality which one finds untouched in animals and in
> most children...[or] among primitive people untouched
> by civilization and often in old Europe peasants who had
> lived all their lives on the soil...[Jung had] that indefinable
> look of the complete, natural human being...[who also]
> had by far the best mind I had ever encountered. (Hannah
> 1991, p. 191, 192)

Jung's connections with the land and "the two million-year-old man within" made important contributions to developing his character. (n 80)

A second major experience for Jung in India revolved around the Indian approach to sexuality. Jung was befuddled by the "exquisitely obscene sculptures" on the temples. He could only imagine young men's minds being filled with sexual fantasies rather than being moved towards enlightenment. His guide told him one has to be made conscious of one's dharma (universal law) and fulfill it before one could achieve spiritualization. (MDR, p. 277, 278) The *Kama Sutra* offers advice on how to live a full sex life as part of becoming a whole person; one of the most powerful Hindu gods is worshipped as a phallus in certain cults. (see n 11) By honoring sexuality as sacred, the Hindus avert an unconscious subterfuge and denigration of this powerful drive. Jung had only to recall the connection between sexuality and spirituality in the relationship of Salome (Eros) and Philemon (Logos). The Judeo-Christian religion, he knew, has a history of suppression of the goddess cults where erotic energy was used as a path to the divine. (see Appendices G and H in volume 3)

Jung's third major experience was the recognition of the essence of the Buddha. He was overcome with emotion by a visit to a Buddhist stupa on the hill of Sanche, India. The stupa was "of immense simplicity, austerity and lucidity" like the Buddha's teaching (CW 10, ¶ 991):

> There is something unspeakably solemn about this place in its exalted loneliness...This place, together with its architecture, its silence, and its peace beyond all turmoils of the heart, its very forgetfulness of human emotions, is truly and essentially Indian; it is as much the "secret" of India as the Taj Mahal is the secret of Islam. (CW 10, ¶ 992)

Jung said he "was deeply moved to the point of complete bewilderment" when "Buddhism dawned on me for the first time"; the Buddha had the same insight about the primal significance of consciousness that he had on the plains of Athi in Africa twelve years earlier (Bair 2003, p. 429):

> I grasped the life of the Buddha as the reality of the self which had broken through and laid claim to a personal life. For Buddha, the self stands above all gods, a *unus mundus* which represents the essence of human existence and of the world as a whole. The self embodies both the aspect of intrinsic being and the aspect of its being known, without which no world exists. Buddha saw and grasped the cosmogonic dignity of human consciousness. (MDR, p. 279)

Christ also embodied the self and overcame the world, but through a foredoomed sacrifice "like an act of destiny." Jung saw Buddha as a more complete being because he was a historical figure and was easier to understand: more is seen and done rather than suffered. (MDR, p. 279) (n 81) "Both paths are right," (p. 279) for in the end the fundamental aim and message are the same: become whole, integrated individuals by becoming fully conscious of oneself. It is necessary to develop the most primal human needs—love and compassion—in order to do this. (p. 353, 354) Psychology and psychoanalysis, the West's great contributions to understanding human behavior, have come to the same conclusion. Attachment theory, whose base is the mother-child bond (the archetypal Christian image is the Madonna and Child), says one cannot become whole and integrated without a deep sense of Eros—

compassion for the personalities within and without—"love thy neighbor *as thyself.*"

To make the construct complete, one must be fully knowledgeable of the unique human niche in nature and develop a consciousness of a proper and sustainable relationship to the natural world. Having an ecological concept of the ego in good relationship to the inner and outer tribes provides an important framework for developing this consciousness, as does Jung's goal of uniting our cultural side with the indigenous one within. We fulfill our human potential by fully engaging our creative, emotional, scientific, artistic and symbolic being in our relation to others and to nature and by recognizing nature as an objective existence. (theme developed in volume 1, chapter 2 and volume 3, Appendix K) (n 82)

The alchemical secret of achieving Buddha or Christ consciousness requires wrestling with archetypal forces so powerful that they are aptly depicted as gods and goddesses. To do that one needs a deep experience of Eros—an ability to have compassion for oneself and for others—and the strength, courage and endurance to be in intimate relationship with the positive and negative forces of "the Other." The path is fearful, isolating, and not without considerable suffering. The ego needs support in this process, metaphorically depicted as the alchemical vessel or sensed as the presence or support of Christ or Buddha. Therapy and such practices as meditation, yoga, centering prayer, etc., can help contain the ego and put one into a state of Buddha or Christ consciousness. This consciousness, the mountaintop perspective, sees the rough and tumble personal experiences in the valley as being the embodiment of the interactions of the gods and goddesses within the framework of an ecopsychological Self.

Jung saw humans as the conscious part of God's creation, the conscious part of God in a sense. We enable God to enter three-dimensional reality and become conscious of Itself. Humans express God and co-create the universe through inspiration and creativity associated with God and by consciously differentiating and giving objective existence to God as manifest in the forms and processes of creation. This concept of a vital human role in completing creation by giving it an objective existence may help Westerners experience nature in a sacred manner—an important goal in ecopsychology.

Jung's insight into Buddhism and his experience of a drumming ceremony supported his idea of the ultimate value of consciousness:

> [Buddha is called] the All-Highest, The Absolute [expressions properly used "only of God"]... By virtue of the power of the gods man is enabled to gain an insight into his Creator. He has even been given the power to annihilate Creation in its essential aspect, that is, man's consciousness of the world...By means of enlightenment...the chain of causality which leads inevitably to old age, sickness, and death—can be broken, so that the illusion of Being comes to an end...A thought and a premonition that have long been present in humanity [is] the idea of the creature that surpasses its creator by a small but decisive factor. (MDR, p. 220)

Jung associated this concept with the literal possibility of destroying creation with radioactivity. He would have put humankind's mass genocide of species into the same category.

Jung noted basic differences in the quest for meaning as presented in Eastern and Western cosmologies. The West is predominately extraverted, projecting meaning into the environment and considering that it exists in objects. The myth is of an evolutionary cosmology with a beginning and a goal with individuals feeling the need to help complete the meaning of the world; the universe must have a meaning. In the East, "the succession of birth and death is viewed as an endless continuity, as an eternal wheel rolling on forever without a goal. Man lives and attains knowledge and dies and begins again from the beginning." (MDR, p. 316) This is a cosmology of "a beginning and mere end,...a static, self-contained, eternal cycle of events." (p. 316, 317) "Only with the Buddha does the idea of a goal emerge, namely, the overcoming of earthly existence." (p. 316) The Eastern man is predominately introverted—trying to embody meaning within himself while "stripping the world and existence from himself." (p. 317) Jung felt both are right; meaning is both within and without, (p. 317) suggesting the possibility of meaning existing without humans—an objective reality of meaning. (n 83)

The two orientations become one because archetypes are like patterns, or fractals, that run through the psychic, organic, and non-organic realms, especially considering the archetype of the organism. An organism can be thought of as a system of nested selves, with many levels operating and interacting simultaneously and each level (self) conducting a particular directed function. With the Self as the archetype of organism, meaning becomes associated with acting in accordance with the consciousness and acceptance of one's place in the fluctuating order and arrangement of the inter-related elements of the inner and outer worlds. (see Appendix C: Self and Organism in volume 1 and the concept of cosmos discussed in Appendix K of volume 3) Consulting the *I Ching* can be particularly helpful in developing this sense of meaning. Enlightenment is not about the dissolution of the world but of realizing the spirit, or soul, in life and *in the world*, of seeing more than just the physical levels of existence.

Jung was deeply moved by a drumming ceremony in a temple tour in Ceylon (Sri Lanka). In the beautiful drumming sacrificed to one's Buddha nature, Jung realized the drum spoke "the ancient language of the belly and solar plexus," engendering a "meditative utterance" that was "but one of the many acts of self-redemption performed by the awakened human being." (MDR, p. 284) The belly and solar plexus speak a deeper language than the heart, "right from the deepest layers of the human soul: the layer of the primeval ancestors and the layers below." (Hannah 1991, p. 252) Paralleling the Buddhists, Native Americans say the drumbeat is the heartbeat of Mother Earth.

After the drum ceremony, Jung saw that "young men and girls poured out enormous mounds of Jasmine flowers in front of the altars, at the same time singing a prayer under their breath: a *mantram*." They were not praying to Buddha, because he is in nirvana, but singing: "This life is transitory as the beauty of these flowers. May my God [*deva*] share with me the merit of this offering." (MDR, p. 283) This was one of the most important impressions India made on him—an illumination of his life-long preoccupation: "The thorny problem of the relationship between eternal man, the self and earthly man in time and space." (p. 322, 323)

The dancers realized their connection to the eternal by acknowledging the transitory nature of life *and* knowing there is more to life than three-dimensional existence in space/time. Maya does not mean that the physical is not real; it means it is a mistake to believe that there is nothing beyond physical reality. Ceremonial dance and music are avenues for the eternal archetypal Self/divine to manifest in time and space in mutual consciousness of dancer and divine. Stated another way, there is a divine and eternal dimension of human experience that can be realized with the aid of ceremonial music and dance—and many other means. In the terms of dynamic systems theory, ceremonial dance and music further the emergence of a state of consciousness phenomenologically described as an experience of the eternal and divine. The eternal-archetypal dimension is consciously realized and experienced.

Jung told Barbara Hannah that India was, in some ways, "the most bewildering experience of his life." (Hannah 1991, p. 248) He eventually found his philosophy: to cultivate "the essence of Greek wisdom, 'Exaggerate nothing, all good lies in right measure'" (CW 12, ¶ 37)—the yellow middle path in the *I Ching*. Hannah related this to a statement in John Gowers' *Confessio amantis*: "A warring peace, a sweet wound, an agreeable evil." (Hannah 1991, p. 248, 249) Jung's sense would be a conscious experience of the Greek concept of *cosmos*, described as "fitting order." This is the beauty of forms presenting themselves and interacting in a proper and timely manner—also a description of the Tao. (see "cosmos" in Appendix K of volume 3)

CHAPTER 12

The Holy Grail and Near Death Experiences

"[India] left tracks which lead from one infinity into another infinity," Jung wrote. (MDR, p. 284) During a hospitalization near the end of his trip, he had many remarkable dreams that underscored his personal myth: to rescue the Grail for Western culture. (n 84) He said a dream he had when just out of the hospital made one of the "most powerful dream impressions" in his life. (Bair 2003, p. 429) The dream location was on what seemed to be an island off the Southern coast of England. His sightseeing companions were not impressed that there was to be a secret celebration of the Grail that night in a medieval castle of the Grail. The lower wall of the castle had a tiny, iron, hooded gnome moving among metal leaves and vines containing tiny iron houses. (n 85) For the celebration to occur that evening, the responsibility fell upon Jung to fetch the Grail at night from a second smaller, desolate island. To do so Jung had to swim across a cold, wide channel. (MDR, p. 280-282) (n 86)

He said the most important aspect of the dream was "the visibility of the Grail or the Grail's castle"—it was to be seen as real. (Bair 2003, p. 429) It was powerful and alive—not a passive tourist attraction as it was to some people in the dream. Ten years previous Jung had discovered that the myth of the Grail was still a living thing in many places in England, "recognized again by poets and prophetically revived" in different forms under changed names. Jung took the dream to mean he should not be preoccupied with India but with what was being lost in the West, symbolized by the quest for the Grail and the philosopher's stone of the alchemists. (MDR, p. 282) (see Appendices D and E) "The Grail is a symbol of enlightenment" in the West he wrote (Bair 2003, p. 430)–the *unum vas, una medicina* and *unus lapis* of the alchemists (MDR, p. 282) while the Buddha represents the enlightened mind in the East. Buddhists strive to attain the degree of fulfillment and perfection of the Buddha.

The ultimate meaning of the Grail lay in its connection with the individuation process of becoming whole where one gives oneself over to the impersonal, that which is beyond and more encompassing than the personal. It is about becoming a Chinese sage: "the ear listening to the Inner King." Individuation is ultimately a mystery—beyond human comprehension—"'a lonely search' perhaps akin to the 'process of dying.'" Jung added, "Only few could bear such a search," symbolized by his swimming alone in the cold water to a desolate island containing the Grail. (Bair 2003, p. 429)

Bair noted that Jung "thought he may have had such dreams... because his overall question was how and why the evil he encountered in India was 'not a moral dimension,' but rather...'a divine power.'" (Bair 2003, p. 429 quoted from the *Protocols*) The India trip "provoked the initial reflections upon religion that served as the basis for all his writings on the subject from then on." (p. 497) Answers to the questions which emerged came years later when Jung used his understanding of alchemy to analyze Christianity and the dark side of God. He developed the position on morals that one should intensely engage the Self in the hope of generating an individual response to a moral conflict, perhaps even doing what is considered to be "wrong" by conventional moral and ethical standards. "India was not my task," Jung wrote, "but only a part of the way—admittedly a significant one—which should carry me closer to my goal." (MDR, p. 282)

The powerful impressions and imagery from India loomed large in a near death experience six years later. Following a massive heart attack, he experienced a series of visions while under oxygen and camphor in February of 1944 at age 68. Jung was at "the outermost border," some-where between "a dream and an ecstasy"—probably between delirium and a coma. The visions, together with his trip to India in 1937-38, which ended in briefer periods of delirium while hospitalized, were the most enormous experiences of his life. (Bair 2003, p. 497)

The 1944 visions altered his life and eventually led him to revamp his concept of the archetypes. One vision was of Jung floating about one thousand miles above Sri Lanka with the earth below "bathed in a glori-ously blue light" and shimmering in intense colors: "The most glorious thing I had ever seen," Jung proclaimed. (MDR, p. 289, 290) In another vision, a Hindu sat in lotus posture waiting for Jung in the entrance to a huge rock in outer space. Deeper in the rock was the entrance to an antechamber framed by a wreath of flaming lamps similar to a temple entrance he had visited in Kandy, Sri Lanka. The lamps represented "a purifying essence through which he had to walk." (Bair 2003, p. 497) As he approached the step to enter the rock, he underwent an extremely painful process of having his entire earthy existence stripped away:

> There was no longer anything I wanted or desired. I existed in an objective form; I was what I had been and lived. At first the sense of annihilation predominated, of having been stripped or pillaged; but suddenly that became of no consequence. (MDR, p. 291)

As soon as he entered the illuminated temple in the rock, he was certain he would meet *his* people who could answer his burning questions about the historical context of his life and the direction in which it had been flowing. As he thought about this he saw his doctor, in his primal form as healer, floating up from Europe. He was delegated by the earth to protest Jung's departure and insisted Jung return immediately. At that moment the vision ceased. (MDR, p. 291, 292)

Jung was profoundly disappointed that he didn't get to enter the temple and join the "greater company" he belonged with. It took him three weeks to decide to live again. (n 87) Reality seemed like a prison, an artificially created three-dimensional world "in which each person sat by himself in a little box" suspended by a thread. (MDR, p. 292) He was depressed, weak and wretched during the day, but woke at midnight for an hour into an utterly transformed, ecstatic, blissful state. "I felt as though I were floating in space," he said, "as though I were safe in the womb of the universe—in a tremendous void, but filled with the highest possible feeling of happiness" (p. 293)—Jung in the pregnant void. Everything around him in the hospital seemed enchanted, a magical, sacred atmosphere with "a *pneuma* of inexpressible sanctity in the room, whose manifestation was the *mysterium coniunctionis.*" (p. 295) He *experienced* the divine union in the form of visions of the Cabbalistic marriage in the afterlife of the male and female principles: he *was* the marriage. Then he *was* the festive Marriage of the Lamb in Jerusalem with ineffable states of joy and angels and light, which led to a vision of Zeus and Hera consummating their marriage in an outdoor amphitheater. The midnight visions gradually mingled and paled as Jung approached life again. They were gone after three weeks. (p. 294, 295)

The sacred marriage and sexual union of divine figures are prime examples of the union of opposites as a symbol of the Self. It illustrates the symbolic dimension of sexuality depicted in Shiva and Shakti in loving embrace, one of the Hindu images for liberation or nirvana. Such symbols of the Self add the important dimension to ecopsychology of the sacredness of sexuality and the body, our most direct link to nature and a sense of the Spirit in nature.

The visions and experiences had seemed utterly real to Jung: "the most tremendous things I had ever experienced," he said. (n 88) By contrast, everything during the day irritated him; everything "was too material, too crude and clumsy, terribly limited both spatially and spiritually." Reality felt like an empty imprisonment, "yet it had a kind of hypnotic power." Jung wrote, "I have never since entirely freed myself of the impression that this life is a segment of existence which is enacted in a three-dimensional boxlike universe especially set up for it." (MDR, p. 295)

Jung's visions "had a quality of absolute objectivity," (MDR, p. 295) an objectivity he later related to a dream-vision he had soon after Emma died in 1955. She appeared to him in her prime wearing her best dress:

> Her expression was neither joyful nor sad, but, rather, objectively wise and understanding, without the slightest emotional reaction, as though she were beyond the mist of affects...It contained the beginning of our relationship, the events of fifty-three years of marriage, and the end of her life also. (p. 296) (n 89)

The dream was an example of the objectivity necessary for a completed individuation: "Only through objective cognition is the real *coniunctio* possible." (MDR, p. 297) Emotional ties contain projections that coerce and constrain both parties. Objective cognition is seeing and accepting the absolute reality of a situation, what Jung called the "mountaintop perspective" related to Winnicott's concept of the use of the object. (Winnicott 1969) Plato said philosophy is being able to die before one's physical death, meaning that facing death, bringing death to life, gives one the objectivity of a philosopher of life. I associate such objective cognition with a perspective that can be obtained by activities like meditation, vision quests, and the moments of deep insight in life and in therapy.

Jung had completed *Psychology and Alchemy* just over a year before the near death visions; he had also written the first chapters of his *opus magnum, Mysterium Coniunctionis*. "All I have written is correct," he said; he felt the illness was necessary for him to know the full reality of the *mysterium coniunctionis*. (Hannah 1991, p. 279)

He suffered another heart attack 2-1/2 years later, in November of 1946, probably as dangerous as the first: he was "suspended over the abyss" for several weeks. (Hannah 1991, p. 293, 294) Jung believed it occurred because he was involved in an intense period of creative activity at that time, wrestling "with the mysterious problem of *hieros gamos* (the *mysterium coniunctionis*)." He felt it took the two heart attacks to understand the *hieros gamos* well enough to even write about it. (p. 294, 295) Eleven years later and four years before his death at age 86 Jung admitted that he had not "solved the riddle of the *coniunctio* mystery" and was "darkly aware of things lurking in the background of the problem—things too big for horizons." (Jung 1976a, p. 393) He, as much as anyone, could appreciate the depth of the meaning of the union of warring opposites; he had been aware of the dark side of God since childhood, had a powerful confrontation with the unconscious, had suffered in Europe through two world wars, and was essentially married to two women!

Fundamental changes occurred in Jung's relationships with the women in his life following his first heart attack in 1944. Emma had rented a room in the hospital and didn't leave the building for over two months. Bair comments:

> Jung's illness struck the death knell for [his] long relationship [with Toni Wolff], which had been imperiled since Toni refused to participate in alchemical research (n 90)...By the time Jung went home, he was as dependent upon Emma as a small child upon his mother. (Bair 2003, p. 501)

Nighttime visions during hospitalizations and dreams of all phases of his long marriage confronted Jung with a sense of wholeness:

> From that time on, he revered [Emma] for all that she had brought to his life, and he sanctified their marriage as "an indescribable whole." (Bair 2003, p. 501)

> A gracious and generous accommodation had sprung up naturally between Toni and Emma sometime in the late 1940s, and it lasted for the remainder of Toni's life. (p. 558)

CHAPTER 13

Fruitful Late Years

Jung's two heart attacks gave him an excuse to curtail public appearances and severely reduce analytic sessions to create free time for research and writing. Occasionally he worked himself to exhaustion and became "moody and rude," sometimes going several days without shaving; behaving "like a woman giving birth to a child" during his most intense periods. People noticed changes in Jung's attitude in the last two decades of his life that began as early as the enforced isolation and introspection of World War II. Jolande Jacobe noted:

> He really wasn't interested in anyone's private life anymore. He was only interested in the 'Big Dreams,' in the collective archetypal world...He was no longer in contact with pulsation of the outer world...Jung lived now in another world. (Bair 2003, p. 528)

He began a fruitful period of work after the first near death experience, writing many of his principle works with the courage to reformulate ideas and surrender to the current of his thoughts. "One problem after the other revealed itself to me and took shape," Jung wrote (MDR, p. 297), particularly while working on his crowning work, *The Mysterium Coniunctionis*. (n 91) *Aion*, published in 1951, examined the two thousand year history of Christianity in an attempt to deal adequately with the problem of the union of opposites. *Answer to Job*, published in 1952 but finished some years earlier, was as an emotional response to God's dark unconscious side as it appeared in the Old Testament and as it evolved through the Christian era. (n 92) Jung had the age (77) and courage to publish on a totally different and equally controversial subject in 1952—"On Synchronicity." Barbara Hannah comments:

> It must have been the experience outside time, when he felt himself to "exist simultaneously the day before yesterday, today and the day after tomorrow," that rendered

him capable of freeing himself from our ingrained habit of thinking in terms of cause and effect, liberating him to think synchronistically and to formulate a whole article entirely from that point of view. (Hannah 1991, p. 309)

Toni Wolff died unexpectedly on March 21, 1953. Her death deeply distressed Jung and exacerbated his hypertension and tachycardia. On Easter Saturday after her death,

he dreamed that Toni visited him, garbed in a dress of many brilliant hues whose primary color was royal blue. He remembered her carriage as regal and floating, majestic and like a bird, a kingfisher or a peacock. (n 93) Although she said nothing in the dream, he awoke feeling comforted. (Bair 2003, p. 559)

Jung carved these words to her in Chinese characters on a small monument placed in a grove of trees near his Kusnacht house: "Toni Wolff. Lotus. Nun. Mysterious." (p. 559)

Emma died a stoic death two years later, in 1955, of stomach cancer that metastasized throughout her body. "[Jung] turned inward and was mostly silent, it was 'touch and go whether he would ever come back.'" (Bair 2003, p. 564) He lovingly carved a beautiful stone at Bollingen that Emma's descendents said "was the most accurate description of how she lived her life: *O vas insigne devotione et obedientia* (O vase, sign of exceptional devotion and obedience)." (p. 322) Jung remarked, "The close of her life, the end, and what it made me realize, wrenched me violently out of myself. It cost me a great deal to regain my footing, and contact with stone helped me." (MDR, p. 175) He spent the first few months after Emma's death carving the names of his paternal ancestors onto stone tablets he later placed at Bollingen. (Hannah 1991, p. 337) He became aware of the "fateful links between me and my ancestors" while carving, feeling charged to address the unanswered questions posed to his forefathers. (MDR, p. 233) Ideas came to him during his stone carvings that became the genesis of important writings. (p. 175)

He had finished all the essential aspects of *Mysterium Coniunctionis* before the beginning of 1955, (Hannah 1991, p. 321) saying it would be his last book. (p. 333) In his eightieth year shortly after Emma's death he wrote in a letter "that it helped him most not to dwell on the past, but to concentrate on why he had to be the survivor, and to give his whole energy to finding the purpose he still had to fulfill." (p. 326) Extending the ego consciousness achieved in old age was the task that kept Jung alive after his wife's death. (p. 330) In the six remaining years of his life he produced several important works. These included *The Undiscovered Self, Flying Saucers: A Modern Myth of Things Seen in the Sky*, "A Psychological View of Consciousness," his autobiography *Memories, Dreams, Reflections*, and the development of *Man and His Symbols*—a book he was working on when he died in 1961 at age 86. The chapter he wrote gives a final and concise explanation of his psychology for the lay person.

CHAPTER 14

The Archetype of Life After Death

One of the most compelling chapters in *Memories, Dreams, Reflections*, "On Life After Death," incorporates the wisdom of Jung's near death experiences and his musings about death. It is an important example of Jung's approach to archetypal material. Jung acknowledged the fact that "without my wishing and without my doing anything about it," ideas about death and a life hereafter arose in him. (MDR, p. 299) Archetypes arise spontaneously from within in pre-conditioned mythic forms as does the *archetype of life after death*. Jung said it was important to speak of incomprehensible things, such as the myth of life after death, even if we can never know for certain what lies behind them. He declared, "I know too little about psychic life to feel that I can set it right out of superior knowledge." He bemoaned the "short shrift" given by moderns to the mythic side of man: "He can no longer create fables." (p. 300) Myths give a certain vital "glamour" to existence and mythologizing is a "healing and valid activity" for the emotions. "A great deal escapes [modern humans]" without myths, said Jung. (p. 300, 301)

Jung recognized the invaluable role played by consciousness and three-dimensional reality in manifesting (incarnating) the archetypal realm of the unconscious *and* the role of myth in communicating between the two realms. Our metaphysical task is to raise conscious-ness and that cannot be done without mythologizing: "Myth is the natural and indispensable intermediate stage between unconscious and conscious cognition." (MDR, p. 311) Jung extended his reflections to the relationship between unconscious and conscious knowledge:

> True, the unconscious knows more than consciousness does; but it is knowledge of a special sort, knowledge in eternity, usually without reference to the here and now, not couched in language of the intellect [Jung's childhood Personality No. 2]. (p. 311)

Jung's idea of unlimited knowledge present in the unconscious is analogous to the unlimited knowledge present in nature, an ecopsychological concept. We see a complex, beautiful, awesome world and science is a powerful means of expanding our consciousness of it. Science uses focused attention, reason and intuition to pose questions, generate hypotheses and search for answers using established procedures and statistics to build upon earlier discoveries and knowledge. Science is now probing deep into brain structure and function and linking it with studies on meditation and imaging techniques: what I call the new alchemy.

Science cannot deal with things that are ultimately unknowable, the proper approach then being to "abandon it as an intellectual [or scientific] problem" (MDR, p. 301) and take note of communications from the unconscious in the forms of dreams, mythic traditions, "synchronistic phenomena, premonitions and dreams that come true." (p. 302) These hints point to a need for a hypothesis about life after death, for "an archetype, rich in secret life,…seeks to add itself to our own individual life in order to make it whole." The more of the myth/unconscious we make conscious and integrate the more whole we are. (p. 302) A person is just as right or wrong to live in a myth about life after death as one who does not believe, "but while the man who despairs marches toward nothingness, the one who has placed his faith in the archetype follows the tracks of life and lives right into his death." (p. 306) "They live more sensibly, feel better, and are more at peace." (p. 301)

Jung thought that if there were life after death it would be in the part of the psyche, demonstrated by synchronicity, that is relative to space and time. That part "seems to increase, in proportion to the distance from consciousness, to an absolute condition of timelessness and spacelessness." (MDR, p. 305) Sleep, near death experiences and the extreme psychic states created by deliberate exercises like vision quests and Sundancing can put one into this realm, the Hermes realm (volume 3). When one is closely associated with a person who dies or is in the season associated with death, i.e., autumn with its Halloween celebration (see volume 4, chapter 6: Seasons of the Soul), easier access is afforded. This realm was acknowledged and honored by all indigenous cultures and exists in the two million-year-old man within each of us. In dynamic systems terms, it can be described as a type of consciousness that can emerge in each of us, particularly when dealing with death issues.

CHAPTER 15

Jung's Pagan Unconscious and the Importance of Earthly Man

Jung gave an example of a dream that hinted of life after death. It underscored the "pagan" unconscious in Personality No. 2 of Jung and his mother and linked No. 2 with a "green" spirituality. He was deeply shaken by news of his mother's sudden death in 1923 that came to him while he was away. He had a frightening dream the night before she died of being in a dense, gloomy, primeval forest with huge trees and boulders. "A piercing whistle that seemed to resound through the whole universe" signaled the arrival of a gigantic wolfhound that tore past Jung. He knew "the Wild Huntsman had commanded it to carry away a human soul," and awoke "in deadly terror." The next morning he received the news of his mother's passing. (MDR, p. 313)

Jung was familiar with

> the "Wild Huntsman, the *"Grunhutl,"* or Wearer of the Green hat, who hunted with his wolves that night—it was the season of Fohn storms in January. It was Wotan, the god of my Alemannic forefathers who had gathered my mother to her ancestors—negatively to the "wild horde," but positively to the *"salig lut,"* the blessed folk. (MDR, p. 313)

Christian missionaries turned Wotan into a devil, but the Romans properly recognized him as Mercury or Hermes,

> a nature spirit who returned to life again in the Merlin of the Grail legend and became, as the *spiritus Mercurialis*, the sought-after arcanum of the alchemists. Thus the dream says that the soul of my mother was taken into *that greater territory of the self which lies beyond the segment of Christian morality, taken into that wholeness of nature and spirit in which conflicts and contradictions are resolved.* (emphasis added) (p. 313, 314)

Jung experienced two violently conflicting feelings as he rode home that night. On the one hand there was great grief and the devastating impression of the dream, "[but] during the entire journey I continually heard dance music, laughter, and jollity, as though a wedding were being celebrated." (MDR, p. 314) The paradox is that from the ego's standpoint death is a catastrophe,

> as if wicked and pitiless powers had put an end to a human life...[But] in the light of eternity, it is a wedding, a *mysterium coniunctionis*. The soul attains, as it were, its missing half; it achieves wholeness. On Greek sarcophagi the joyous element was represented by dancing girls, on Etruscan tombs by banquets. (p. 314, 315)

Jung's response to his mother's death illustrates the relationship of the temporal to the eternal, of three-dimensional reality to timelessness and spacelessness, of the individual to the archetypal. The archetype of death is as important in nature as the archetype of life; indeed it is its compliment. The death archetype in humans generates a spiritualizing experience associated with the *hieros gamos* (sacred union) as Jung described in his nighttime visions following his near death experience.

An illuminating dream after his near death experience in 1944 revealed the relationship between eternal man, the self, and earthly man in time and space. He dreamt he had come upon a yogi in a small mountain chapel. The yogi was in deep meditation and wore Jung's face. Jung awoke in profound fright with the thought that the yogi was meditating Jung: "'He has a dream, and I am it.' I knew that when he awakened, I would no longer be." (MDR, p. 323)

Jung understood the dream as a parable. When the self "renounces existence in the hereafter," it assumes a religious posture and meditates a *particular* earthly form, in this case Jung. It does this to increase consciousness and clarity by being in three-dimensional reality. Ego consciousness sees this causal process in the reverse: "From that point we look out upon an enigmatic world of obscurity, never knowing to what extent the shadowy forms we see are caused by our consciousness, or possess a reality of their own." (n 94) Jung adds, "as a rule the images of the unconscious are not produced by consciousness, but have a reality and spontaneity of their own." (MDR, p. 323, 324) (see appendix K in volume 3) Mandala symbols that spontaneously arise from the unconscious hint that the Self is implicit wholeness and ultimate reality. The dream suggests that,

> in the opinion of the "other side," our unconscious exis-
> tence is the real one and our conscious world a kind of illu-
> sion, an apparent reality constructed for a specific purpose,
> like a dream which seems a reality as long as we are in it.
> (p. 324)

Jung's expanded understanding of the dream is that wholeness, individuation, and a connection to the infinite are the only worthy goals
in life. The main goal in life should be a striving for total consciousness
and self-awareness:

> Attainment of consciousness is culture in the broadest
> sense, and self-knowledge is therefore the heart and essence
> of this process. The Oriental attributes unquestionably
> divine significance to the self, and according to the ancient
> Christian view self-knowledge is the road to knowledge of
> God. (MDR, p. 324, 325)

Full consciousness has a cultural aspect because it entails an awareness of the archetypal dimension of human experience, the eternal
and infinite dimension whose components, the archetypes, run like
a pattern/fractal from the intra-psychic through a culture's systems,
myths and religion. Only when we are related to the infinite can we
break our bondage to the unsatisfactory life of materialism and consum-
erism with its accompanying envy and jealousy. Jung had this to say as
he looked back over his life in his late years:

> If we understand and feel that here in this life we already
> have a link with the infinite, desires and attitudes change.
> *In the final analysis, we count for something only because of the
> essential we embody, and if we do not embody that, life is wasted.*
> In our relationships to other men, too, the crucial question
> is whether an element of boundlessness is expressed in the
> relationship.(emphasis added) (MDR, p. 325)

A paradox is that only by becoming conscious of our limitations can
we approach the infiniteness of the unconscious and not be obliterated
by it as Jung was by Personality No. 2 in his youth. "In such awareness
we experience ourselves concurrently as limited and eternal, as both
the one and the other." (MDR, p. 325) To find one's myth and to realize
what phase of a typical (archetypal) process one is in is to find where the
infinite touches one's life, for archetypes are of the impersonal/trans-
personal, eternal realm. The uniqueness of each archetype is seen in the
distinctly different characters of the gods and goddesses, the distinct

qualities of the interactions between the different combinations of gods and goddesses, and the phases of their relationships. By knowing our limits, such as our psychological type, and the particular archetypes that live through us, we sense our uniqueness as well as our link to the eternal archetypal. Astrological charts are good examples of how each person's combination of basic human traits are associated with the gods and goddesses who rule those traits and the phases of their interactions over time. A strongly introverted thinking type may look with envy, disdain, or appreciation upon the smooth-talking extraverted feeling type in a group situation. She in turn may be gifted (by the gods) in mathematics and music in ways others can respect and admire.

Hubris and inflation plague the individual who has not differentiated himself or herself from the collective power of the archetype. The first step is to identify the archetypes living through one and then put oneself in a position of gratefulness and respect for the powers in the manner of paying homage to a god or goddess. (Native Americans find their archetypal core on vision quests where their spirit animal comes to them to energize and inform their lives.) One must then discern where one's archetype fits in with the Gestalt of all activated archetypes at different levels of the Self, as illustrated by Jung's Liverpool dream and other mandala symbolism. The Self as the archetype of the organism at its many levels represents a total ecology of the soul.

As we realize how we embody a particular archetype or combination of archetypes—how we are a unique expression of eternal forms (what Jung called "embodying the essential")—we develop our connection to the infinite and life takes on deeper meaning. One may consult the *I Ching* to delineate which of 4096 possible archetypal life situations one is living out at the moment. The goal is to be in the Tao, "the head that walks." Tao is consciously being aware of, and responding appropriately to, the archetypal background at its many levels within the culture and in the natural environment and not getting trapped in maya—the illusion that physical reality is all there is.

The entrée to the archetypal realm is often through our wounded side. The parts we fear, flee, neglect, and ignore consequently have no consciousness brought to them and they gravitate towards the negative end of the archetypal pole. Only by entering reality—time and space—and allowing ourselves to be drawn into life by our drives and passions and sexuality, can archetypes get constellated (classical description) or emerge (DST). Over time, the archetype unfolds, reveals itself, takes on form from our life experiences that cluster around the archetypal core.

In DST terms this is described as emerging in a self-organizing manner into the archetypal dimension of human experience. A theme is gradually revealed from a confusing array of personal life experiences. When we realize there is a story line, the theme, that unites the elements of our lives, we are on our way to sensing the archetype: the eternal, the mythic, manifesting through our lives.

The core lesson of Jung's life is that our destiny as humans is to become as conscious as possible. To do that we must have a sense of the transcendent realm:

> Our age has shifted all emphasis to the here and now, and thus brought about a daemonization of man and his world...Man has been robbed of transcendence by the shortsightedness of the super-intellectuals. Like them, he has fallen victim to unconsciousness...Man's task is...to become conscious of the contents that press upward from the unconscious. Neither should he persist in the unconsciousness, nor remain identical with the unconscious elements of his being, thus evading his destiny, which is to create more and more consciousness. *As far as we can discern, the sole purpose of human existence is to kindle a light in the darkness of mere being.* It may even be assumed that just as the unconscious affects us, so the increase in our consciousness affects the unconscious. (emphasis added) (MDR, p. 326) (n 95)

Jung was able to fully embody the eternal, to individuate, by following the Hermetic path of the alchemists. At Bollingen, his "confession in stone" he associated with Merlin's retreat, he experienced and articulated what it is to journey through life as a follower of Hermes, the theme which I will turn to in volume 3 of *The Dairy Farmer's Guide*. The psychological system that made him the prototypical ecopsychologist arose in good part from his connection with nature and the archetypal realm he experienced at Bollingen. We see this in the final comments in his autobiography:

> The world into which we are born is brutal and cruel, and at the same time of divine beauty...Life is—or has—meaning and meaninglessness. I cherish the anxious hope that meaning will preponderate and win the battle.
>
> When Lao-tzu says: "All are clear, I alone am clouded," he is expressing what I now feel in advanced old age. Lao-tzu ...at the end of his life desires to return into his own being,

> into the eternal unknowable meaning. The archetype of the old man who has seen enough is eternally true...Yet there is so much that fills me: plants, animals, clouds, day and night, and the eternal in man. The more uncertain I have felt about myself, the more there has grown up in me a feeling of kinship with all things. (MDR, p. 358, 359)

Jung gave a talk at the Zurich Jung Institute late in his life (May 1959) that encapsulated the wisdom of his life's journey. He told the students that with the guidance of dreams and various forms of active imagination one can establish a relationship with the unconscious and nature within. Psychoanalysis may facilitate the process:

> Analysis is a long discussion with the Great Man—an unintelligent attempt to understand him...Work until the patient can see this...You learn about the peculiar intelligence of the background; you learn the nature of the Great Man. You learn about yourself against the Great Man— against his postulates...

> The way is ineffable. One cannot, one *must* not, betray it. It is like the way of Zen—like a sharp knife, and also twisting like a serpent. One needs faith, courage, and no end of honesty and patience. (Jung 1977, p. 360, 361)

CHAPTER 16

Jung's Last Dream

Jung died on June 6, 1961, two months shy of his 86th birthday. His success at following the guidance of the Great Man on his serpentine path through life is reflected in the last dream he communicated to his housekeeper a few days before his death. He saw a big round stone in a high barren place, engraved with the words: "This shall be a sign unto you of wholeness and oneness." Then he saw many pottery vases on the right side of a square. Fibrous roots came out of the ground from a square of trees and surrounded Jung. Gold threads were gleaming among the roots. (Hannah 1991, p. 347)

Hannah's interpretation begins with the sphere as a symbol of unity and wholeness. Recall the huge stone in space Jung was about to enter in his near death experience. Hannah reminds us the ancient Egyptians kept parts of the dismembered corpse of Osiris in pots from which the resurrection was expected to occur. "The old Greeks kept pots in their houses full of wheat seeds. The pots and the soil represented the underworld and the seed the dead waiting for resurrection." (Hannah 1991, p. 347) Jung said,

> Life has always seemed to me like a plant that lives on its rhizome [underground stem as with ferns]. Its true life is invisible, hidden in the rhizome. The part that appears above ground lasts only a single summer...I have never lost a sense of something that lives and endures underneath the eternal flux. What we see is the blossom, which passes. The rhizome remains. (MDR, p. 4)

Von Franz adds a comment on the stone and the gold thread among the roots in the dream: "When the Tao, the meaning of the world and eternal life are attained, the Chinese say, 'Long life flowers with the essence of the stone and the brightness of gold.'" (von Franz 1975, p. 287)

Jung had become the stone he sat upon as a child.

NOTES

1. In examining Jung's life, I will draw on an excellent book by Deirdre Bair, *Jung: A Biography*, to compliment Jung's autobiography, *Memories, Dreams, Reflections* (1961) (referenced in the text as MDR) and Barbara Hannah's *Jung: His Life and Work*. Jung wrote his autobiography in a manner that was "a bit blunt and crude," reflecting an aspect of his character, and feared it would be "auntified." (Bair 2003, p. 611; p. 842 note 147) Bair describes how Jung's writings were toned down by his co-author and Jungian analyst Aniela Jaffe and from pressure from family members. (p. 611; p. 845 note 15; p. 657 note 7) Bair had access to several manuscripts (*Protocols*) that preceded the final typeset, many of which included Jung's handwritten comments. Sonu Shamdasani also had access to the *Protocols* and other private materials. He critiqued Bair and other biographers in his book, *Jung Stripped Bare by His Biographers, Even*. I also draw on biographical material from Marie-Louise von Franz's *C. G. Jung: His Myth in Our Time* to put Jung's life into an archetypal framework.

2. Years ago when I described Jung to a German friend he said: "That sounds like a Swiss. They have a mystical side."

3. I got a taste of what it must have been like in Jung's time by attending St. Nicklaus Abend in Kusnacht-am-Rigi, a small town on the shores of Lake Lucerne. This December 6th event begins at dusk with a group of young men in white tunics parading through the streets. They periodically stop and in unison crack huge bull whips about ten feet long. It sounds like a battery of .22 rifles being fired at close range. The men are followed by a procession of children around a figure dressed much like our Santa Claus—their St. Nicklaus, or *Sammi Klaus* in Schweizerdeutsch. The finale is a small army of men lugging huge Swiss cowbells. The earth and all human parts rumble from the unbearable din. Such is the intent; the activities are meant to energize the earth and the earth within us, waking it up from its wintry repose. My analyst, herself from a small Swiss town, said many such events survived until World War II, after which most died out. She was terrified as a child by people coming to her home wearing frightening masks associated with certain festivals.

4. Barbara Hannah said, "Almost the majority of Swiss voters came from a peasant background and are still firmly rooted both in the soil and in their instincts." (Hannah 1991, p. 12) As an adult Jung was able to avoid the trappings of polite society and he understood the harsh realities of nature and life on the land. He was fond of some uncles

who "were very deeply rooted in the soil and full of natural wisdom." (p. 29) He loved the Swiss peasant (p. 12) and even as a world famous analyst remained on good terms with simple local people. They talked freely with him and told him of their problems. Jung said many of them had a better understanding of the essential meaning of his books than the academics. (p. 35) He learned from them a respect for wood and stone, enjoying woodcutting all his life and was recognized for his understanding and handling of stone. (p. 35, 36)

5. "Catholicism and Catholic priests induced a certain degree of terror throughout [Jung's] life," Bair writes. (Bair 2003, p. 72; also see p. 24) Speculation is that a priest sexually assaulted Jung—a man he once "worshipped." The priest was a best friend of Jung's father and he vacationed with him. Jung lived with him briefly at age 14. (p. 71, 72)

6. As a psychiatrist, Jung noted that children's dreams often contain significant archetypal motifs. (Jung 1964, p. 73) It was his childhood nightmare that introduced Jung to a living experience of the archetypal realm.

7. Although Jung preferred a symbolic interpretation of the phallus dream, "as an analyst he had frequently linked an 'undervaluation of sexuality' with the self 'symbolized as a phallus.'" (Bair 2003, p. 24) "Undervaluation can consist in an ordinary repression or in overt devaluation," he wrote. "A purely biological interpretation and evaluation of sexuality can have the same effect" as in Freudian psychology that "overlooks the spiritual and 'mystical' implications of the sexual instinct." (CW 9, II, ¶ 357)

8. Von Franz conveys Jung's understanding that "the first dream which one can recall often sets forth in symbolic form...the essence of an entire life, or of the first part of life. It reflects, so to speak, a piece of 'inner truth' into which the individual was born." (von Franz 1975, p. 17) A dream of this immensity was known as a "big" dream by tribal peoples and considered to be of tribal significance; of having meaning for the whole community. The Greek and Roman civilizations shared this belief in big dreams and reported them to the Aeropagus or to the Senate.

9. Jung related the nightmare to the birth of his intellectual life. The ancient Romans believed the phallus symbolized a man's secret "genius" and made sacrifices to it on his birthday. (von Franz 1975, p. 19) It was seen as the source of his physical and mental creative power and the dispenser of his inspired ideas. Jung had a tremendous amount of physical and psychological energy in his adult life and felt driven by his creative genius. (von Franz 1975, p. 22; MDR, p. 356-358) Marie-Louise von Franz, Jung's closest collaborator, noted that "Jung was direct and primitively vital to a rare degree...He met men, things and ideas with his whole being, in a genuine confrontation." (von Franz 1975, p. 20)

The Romans also associated the phallus with a buoyant joy of life (*joie de vivre*). Jung was able to create a jovial festive atmosphere around him, was cheerful and open to any kind of joke (von Franz 1975, p. 19), and was noted for his deep, primal laugh. (p. 280)

The phallus is related to Eros, Aphrodite's consort (Cupid in Roman mythology), and associated with relationship. Von Franz observed Jung's "extraordinary...gift of empathy, almost to the point of being mediumistic." (von Franz 1975, p. 19) He had deep sympathy, warmth and openness for others irregardless of race or status. These qualities of Eros lend themselves to a third archetypal association with the phallus and major determinant in Jung's life—that of doctor and healer. The ancient phallic god was known in antiquity "as Telesphoros, a guide of Asklepios, the god of medical healing...The name Telesphoros means 'he who brings completeness'; he is a god of inner transformation." (p. 23) See Appendix H: Jung's Phallic Self-Image for development of this theme.

10. Jung saw the chthonic, especially sexuality, as being the dark side of God. Sexuality provides an important link, especially for men, to the body and the instinctual, more animal side of human nature. Heinrich Zimmer's *Myths and Symbols in Indian Art and Civilization* (1946) presents a Hindu myth about Shiva as a sacred phallus. It reveals significant archetypal links with Hermes who I see as the god of ecopsychology and who was worshipped in one form as a phallus.

* * * * *

The myth of "The Origin of the Lingam" (*lingobhava*) opens with the familiar primeval situation: no universe, only water and the starless night of the lifeless interval between dissolution and creation. In the infinite ocean all the seeds, all the potentialities, of subsequent evolution rest in a dormant state of undifferentiation. Vishnu, the anthropomorphic embodiment on this fluid of life, is floating...in and upon the substance of his own essence. In the form of a luminous giant he is recumbent on the liquid element, radiant with the steady glow of his blessed energy.

But now a new and astonishing event: Vishnu perceives, all of a sudden, another luminous apparition, and it is approaching him with the swiftness of light, shinning with the brilliance of a galaxy of suns. It is Brahma, the fashioner of the universe, the four-headed one, full of yogic wisdom. Smiling, this new arrival inquires of the recumbent giant: "Who are you? How did you originate? What are you doing here? I am the first progenitor of all beings; I am He Who Originated from Himself!"

Vishnu begged to differ. "On the contrary," he protested, "it is I who am the creator and the destroyer of the universe. I have created and destroyed it time and again."

The two mighty presences proceeded to contest each other's claims and to quarrel. And while they were arguing in the timeless void, presently they perceived rising out of the ocean a towering lingam crowned with flame. Rapidly it grew into infinite space. The two divinities, ceasing their discussion, regarded it with amazement. They could measure neither its height nor its depth.

Brahma said: "You plunge; I shall fly upward. Let us try to discover its two ends."

The two gods assumed their well known animal forms, Brahma the gander, Vishnu the boar. The bird winged into the heavens, the boar dove into the deep. In the opposite directions, on and on, they raced but could attain to neither limit; for while the boar descended and Brahma climbed, the lingam grew and grew.

Presently the side of the prodigious phallus burst open, and in the niche-like aperture the lord of lingam stood revealed, Shiva, the force supreme of the universe. While Brahma and Vishnu bowed before him in adoration, he solemnly proclaimed himself to be the origin of them both. Indeed, he announced himself as a Super-Shiva: the triad of Brahma, Vishnu, and the Shiva, Creator, Maintainer, the Destroyer, he at once contained and bodied forth. Though emanating from the lingam, they, nevertheless, abode permanently within it. They were parts of it, constituents, Brahma the right side, Vishnu the left, but the center was Shiva-Hara, "The Re-absorber, He Who Takes Back or Takes Away."

Thus Shiva appears augmented in the lingam, heightened, enhanced, as the all comprising, basic element. The role for the destroyer now is only one of his three principal manifestations. Side by side with Brahma the Creator and Vishnu the Maintainer, Shiva the Destroyer co-exists in Shiva the Supreme. (Zimmer 1946, p. 128-130)

11. This glorious, eternal dimension of life experienced by children is expressed in Wordsworth's "Intimations of Immortality from Recollections of Early Childhood." (Hannah 1991, p. 23)

12. There are many archetypal associations with the stone Jung put with his childhood manikin to be the manikin's store of vitality. Stone is an age-old symbol for the eternal and enduring in man from which he draws the strength he needs to live. Stone Age men kept stones in special hiding places as repositories of their strength. The churingas of Australian aborigines are either stones or pieces of wood believed to have magic life forces residing within. Many different peoples pile up stones on graves to represent that which survives death. The ancient Germans arranged "Bautar" stones on graves and presented sacrifices there. Souls of dead ancestors were believed to live in the stones and migrated to newborn children. (von Franz 1975, p. 219, 220)

A stone represents the part of a person than can outlast everything. It stands for an inner strength: one cannot be dissolved by inner problems or collective influences just as Jung turned to his manikin and stone when he felt inwardly at odds with himself as a boy. (von Franz 1975, p. 219, 220)

13.

> There is no better means of intensifying the treasured feeling of individuality than the possession of a secret which the individual is pledged to guard...

> The individual's task [is] to differentiate himself from all the others and stand on his own feet. All collective identities, such as membership in organizations, support of "isms," and so on, interfere with the fulfillment of this task...Collective organization is still so essential today that many consider it, with some justification, to be the final goal...

> It may be that in all the garbs, shapes, forms, modes, and manners of life offered [a person] does not find what is peculiarly necessary for him. He will go alone and be his own company. He will serve as his own group, consisting of a variety of opinions and tendencies—which need not necessarily be marching in the same direction...The disunion within himself may cause him to give up, to lapse into identity with his surroundings. (MDR, p. 342, 343)

> Only a secret which the individual cannot betray—one which he fears to give away, or which he cannot formulate in words, and which therefore seems to belong to the category of crazy ideas—can prevent the otherwise inevitable retrogression. (p. 343, 344)

15. Jung hated school. He felt a "sheer terror and torture" over the incomprehensibility of math. (MDR, p. 29) He did not like being told what to draw or how to move: "I always wanted to know at the start to what and to whom I was intrusting myself." He associated this with "a certain physical timidity...linked with a distrust of the world and its potentialities...[that were] filled with vague and incomprehensible perils." (p. 29, 30) As an adult he speculated this may have arisen from the abandonment he felt when his mother left him for several months as a child. (p. 30)

16. The early Gnostics held "a similar idea of the *felix culpa*, the blessed sin which brings about redemption," but Christian tradition emphasized original sin as "an entirely reprehensible act of disobedience to God's will." (Hannah 1991, p. 45)

17. The Lakota Sioux experience *Wakinyan*—The Great Spirit of the West as it manifests in the thunderstorm on the Great Plaines, with awe

and reverence. Like a fearful beast it destroys old, destructive forms, allowing new forms to emerge that are nourished by the rains that accompany a storm. (Rice 1991, p. 120-122)

18. A current hypothesis by Terrance Deacon, who studies semiotic processes underlying animal and human communication, especially language, is that our sense of self is the virtual reality of a symbolic self. Deacon's position is that "consciousness of self...implicitly includes consciousness of other selves, and other consciousnesses can only be represented through the virtual reference created by symbols." It is a symbolic self "that is the source of one's experience of intentionality," judgments and fear of death. (Deacon 1997, p. 452 quoted in Hogenson 2004b, p. 77) (see Appendix B: Bootstrapping the Archetypes in volume 3 of *The Dairy Farmer's Guide*) What, for example, is the reality of their body that an anorexic sees in a mirror? The "security blanket" (transitional object) is the first experience of virtual reality for an infant and forms the basis for symbolic play, creativity and ultimately the religious experience. (Winnicott 1951, p. 229-242) (see Appendix F: Winnicott's Transitional Object in volume 3)

19. Jung said "it was precisely my father's faults and inadequacies that made him particularly lovable to me." (MDR, p. 79)

20. Emma was educated, strong willed, and her strong introverted sensation function helped anchor in reality Jung's highly developed intuition. She shared many interests with Carl and eventually became a sophisticated analyst in her own right. "She...provided her husband with objectivity, balanced judgment, and occasional sharp criticism when she appraised his work." (Bair 2003, p. 181) Freud liked and respected Emma, describing her as "charming, clever, and ambitious." (p. 193)

21. The famous German psychologist, Gustav Aschaffenburg, exemplified the disparagement many in the academic community felt about Freud. "[He] called Freud's method 'wrong in most cases, objectionable in many, and superfluous in all.'" (Bair 2003, p. 102)

22. Freud rushed his version of the *History of Psychoanalysis* into print after the split with Jung and decreed, "Psychoanalysis is my creation...no one can know better than I do what psychoanalysis is." (*History of Psychoanalysis*, in *The Jungians: A Comparative and Historical Perspective*, Routledge: London and Philadelphia, 2000, p. 7 quoted in Bair 2003, p. 241)

23. Jung said in an interview, "God, if [Freud] had only gotten over himself...But there was this neurotic element. If he had gotten over *that*...it would have been crazy...to ever want anything other than to work with him." (Bair 2003, p. 117) One severe neurotic symptom Jung observed was Freud's "propensity to urinate when he found himself in a public place where there was no toilet"—an urge so great he couldn't control it. Jung started to analyze Freud on this matter during their trip to America, but Freud would not provide personal, delicate details out

of fear of risking his authority. Jung believed these details were related to Freud's alleged sexual relationship with his sister-in-law Minna who lived with them. Minna confided this information to Jung on his first visit to Vienna. (p. 164)

Paul Roazen, author of *Freud and His Followers*, writes: "The important matter is what Minna meant to Freud...and not so much the specifics of a possible sexual liaison between them. Freud seemed to have a split it his love life, his sexuality remaining with Martha and his spiritual involvement shifting to Minna." (1992, Da Capo Press: New York, p. 59-63 quoted in Bair 2003, p. 689 note 51)

Freud was the prince in his mother's eye, the oldest child and only son. He had an upset stomach every time he returned from the Sunday meal he shared alone with his mother in her old age. He was humiliated as a child by his father and resented the subjection his father endured from the anti-Semitism in the relatively liberal city of Vienna in the late 1800s. These critical facts together with the sexual relationship with his sister-in-law informed Freud's theory that everything was sexual, the Oedipal conflict was the only archetype, and its roots could be traced back via genetic memory to a primal horde when sons overthrew an unjust, authoritarian father and incestuously made off with their mother.

Bair includes an earlier, less edited version of Jung's house-of-many-levels dream in her biography that says there were "several partially decayed human skulls without lower jaws, obviously the victims of violence, as the tops were forcibly bashed in." (Bair 2003, p. 177) Freud focused on this element when analyzing the dream (p. 178) because it may have constellated Freud's authority and father-murder complex. Jung said every psychology is a confession of the proponent of that psychology, so we can hypothesize that Freud had a father-murder, or incest, complex based on his theory.

Jung said, "'medical discretion' did not permit him to use most of what he knew about Freud." (CGJ to Kurt Wolff, June 4, 1958, Helene Wolff Archives, Beinecke Library, Yale University quoted in Bair 2003, p. 597) "Regards last longer than life," Jung said in a 1959 BBC interview after refusing to respond to a request for personal details about Freud. (Jung 1977, p. 432)

Jung did note a more fundamental problem of Freud's:

> He said [regarding an opinion on a matter], "Yes it is, it must be so!" and I asked why and he said, "Because after all I thought it!" When he thought something, then he was himself surprised by it and then it *had* to be right! Then it damn well had to be right! And that's what later made me think that he in his emotional life—he was delicately sensitive—was once disturbed somehow, severely disturbed. And that originally he wasn't a thinker at all, but began

> to think secondarily, and with difficulty...When feeling has been scared off, one escapes into thinking! (C.G. Jung to Dr. Kurt Eissler, August 29, 1953, Manuscript Division, Library of Congress, Tape no. 74 quoted in Bair 2003, p. 722 note 50).

The emotional wounds probably contributed to other traits Jung saw in Freud: "'[He was] bitter and resentful, hard, cynical.'" (Bair 2003, p. 731 note 52) Jung shared with Freud many of these types of emotional wounds (see Appendix G: Jung's Eros Wound and his Image of God)

Jung said of Freud's work with his dreams: "[His] negative judgments could continuously hurt you without your noticing it. He had to regard everything...from the negative side." (Bair 2003, p.178)

24. Part two of *Symbols* also denied the primacy of sex in libido theory. Freud initially linked libido energy entirely with sexuality, much later adding "ego instincts" and the superego. Jung associated libido with a broader and more general psychic or life energy. (see "On Psychic Energy," CW 8, p. 3-66)

25. Thomas B. Kirsch noted "that Freudians and other schools of psychoanalysis generally accept C. G. Jung's work until approximately 1913, after which they fault him for deviating from scientific methodology." (Bair 2003, p. 679 note 7)

In 1914 after *Symbols* was published, Freud castigated Jung for his self interests and his "'misconceptions of psychoanalysis and his deviations from it.'" (Bair 2003, p. 246) See note 22.

26. Ernest Jones, a chief spokesman for Freud, wrote to Freud in 1913 that Jung was "mentally deranged to a serious extent." (Paskauskas 1993, p.1999 quoted in Shamdasani 2005, p. 72) Freud and the early psychoanalysts used Jung's so-called madness "to explain his defection from psychoanalysis. Consequently, his work could simply be dismissed as the product of a psychosis...After Freud, this view was repeated by psychoanalysts and has had a major propaganda effect." (Shamdasani 2005, p. 72) Sonu Shamdasani chronicled a list of biographies of Jung through the years (p. 72-86) that have continued this "psychoanalytic character assassination," generally depicting his "confrontation with the unconscious" after the break with Freud and his subsequent work on that material as Jung making "a psychology out of a psychosis." (p. 73) Shamdasani noted that both Jung and Freud "sought to invalidate the other's theoretical position by reducing it to being nothing other than the expression of personal psychopathology." (p. 52)

27. Toni Wolff went into analysis with Jung in 1910. She was 22 and Jung was 35 and "the first in a long line of women who gravitated to Jung because he allowed them to use their intellectual interests and abilities in the service of analytical psychology." (Bair 2003, p. 199)

28. Jung began to treat 19 year old Sabina Spielrein when she was hospital-
    ized in Burgholzli in 1904. (Bair 2003, p. 86) Five years after meeting
    Spielrein their relationship entered a deep, intimate phase when Jung
    started relating to her as soul mate and confessor. (p. 151, 152) It was
    1909, Jung (age 34) had been married for six years, and Emma was
    pregnant with their fourth child. This was the first of three times over
    their 52 years of marriage that Emma threatened divorce, and Jung
    changed course. (p. 191, 688 note 23)

    Jung was intrigued by Spielrein, who "was light-years beyond
    [Emma] in worldliness and sophistication" and had an air of exoti-
    cism about her dress. As a Russian Jew she "represented the wildness
    of all that was foreign" and as a visitor "was allowed more kinds of
    freedom than any Swiss woman could even dream about." This medi-
    cal student "was fearlessly outgoing and never hesitated to express her
    views" to anyone. Emma in contrast to Spielrein was docile, domestic,
    shyly retiring and deferential, whose "natural serenity was frequently
    mistaken for bland dullness." (Bair 2003, p. 91) Jung described Emma
    as "'an ordinary [i.e., Swiss] woman and accordingly only interested in
    what interested her husband.'" (p. 93)

    Jung shared with Spielrein his fears about his work, goals and
    handling success. He told her about the painful memories of child-
    hood flooding his mind and how he was looking for "someone who
    knew how to love without 'punishing, locking in, draining the other.'"
    He needed "'passionate, ever changing love'" and pitied any woman
    he loved "for dreaming of 'infinite faithfulness'"—something he was
    incapable of. (Bair 2003, p. 152)

29. Another level of interpretation is that the hero represents what we
    value the most, which Jung personally associated with the force and
    efficiency of his intellect, his superior function. Deposing the hero as
    this representation allowed "for other sides of the personality to be
    born into life." (Bair 2003, p. 727 note 13)

30. Jung's gymnasium schoolmates had called him "Father Abraham"
    and when together with Toni "he seemed the prototype of the wise
    old man, she had a quality of eternal youth." (Hannah 1991, p. 117)
    Barbara Hannah said of all the women she had ever known, Toni Wolff
    was "most fitted to carry the projection of [an anima] figure...She
    could look far more than beautiful, more like a goddess than a mortal
    woman." (p. 118)

31. Simon Magus of the Gnostic tradition went about with a young girl
    from a brothel named Helen who was the re-incarnation of the Trojan
    Helen. (MDR, p. 182) Lao-tzu had his dancing girl. The archetype of
    the older man and the younger woman is portrayed in the movie, *The
    Memoirs of a Geisha.*

32. The phallic aspect of snakes and their symbolic association with the
    unconscious is connected with Hermes. Hermes is closest to, yet can
    reflect, the unconscious, often personified as feminine for a man.

Hermes is closely related to Eros, Aphrodite's consort. The powerful activation of Jung's unconscious found a woman, Toni Wolff, for the projection of his soul image. See volume 3, Appendix H: The Black Goddess and Appendix G: The Sacred Prostitute and the Erotic Feminine for descriptions of the powerful transformative dimension of the erotic feminine.

33. The intensity of Jung's involvement with Toni Wolff in 1914 and the agony and chaos it caused in Jung's life lends some credence to Bair's understanding that the dream of the dove turning into a young woman occurred around Christmas of 1913 and not 1912 as recorded in *Memories, Dreams, Reflections*. (Bair 2003, p. 242) Bair, working with the *Protocols*, said Jung:

> describes this dream as his earliest attempt to explore the unconscious...equat[ing] any knowledge and insight gained at this time with "[falling] in love with women" and "say[ing] yes to it." He said it was the time when the "anima" was first manifested, but he did not yet understand its significance. (Bair 2003, p. 727 note 10)

Shamdasani, who examined many of the sources Bair used, cautions against taking as established fact "the much speculation and rumor... surround[ing] Jung's relations with his female patients." (Shamdasani 2005, p. 112) He could not find conclusive proof in the sources Bair and others mentioned and "will, for the time being, give little credence to such allegations until documents are presented in the public domain." (p. 115)

34. Shamdasani could find no evidence that Jung practiced yoga after 1917. (Shamdasani 2005, p. 108, 109) Jung cautioned Westerners about adopting Eastern practices like yoga. (p. 110) He remained interested in the symbolism of yoga and its parallelism to the individuation process (p. 110, 111) just as he found a book by a Chinese Zen Buddhist to be using "different words for the same reality." (Jung 1977, p. 467)

35. Von Franz recognized Jung as "the first to discover the spontaneous creativity of the unconscious psyche and to follow it consciously." (von Franz 1975, p. 4) The psyche is "the source of *all* human activities" (p. 4) and "the autonomous creative matrix of normal psychic life." (p. 6)

36. R.C.F. Hull, a trusted friend and Jung's translator, briefly saw the *Red Book* years later and described it as being filled with "'disturbing, really mad drawings'"; the "'work of a lunatic'" who had developed the remarkable ability to objectively observe and understand what was happening to himself. (Bair 2003, p. 292, 293; p. 617) Both Hull and psychoanalyst D.W. Winnicott described Jung as a man who healed himself from a psychotic experience, becoming a wounded healer in the tradition of shamans. (D. Winnicott, 1963, Review of *Memories, Dreams, Reflections*. *Journal of Analytical Psychology* 8(2): 173-175). Sonu Shamdasani is one

of the few people to make a scholarly study of both of Jung's personal books and he found "no evidence which would support such a diagnosis" that the fantasies were psychotic. (Shamdasani 2005, p. 95)

Hull proposed a quotation from Coleridge's *Notebooks* to be a motto for Jung's autobiography: "He looked at his own Soul with a Telescope. What seemed all irregular, he saw and shewed to be beautiful Constellations: and he added to the Consciousness hidden worlds within worlds." (quoted in Bair 2003, p. 617)

37. Beyond serving as a sounding board and devil's advocate, Wolff helped Jung to "identify, define, and even name some of the concepts within his analytic system—the 'sensation' function in the *Types* book, the 'anima' and 'animus,' and 'persona.'" (Bair 2003, p. 293)

38. Shamdasani states he has evidence that Emma Jung had not been forbidden from reading the *Black Books*. (Shamdasani 2005, p. 97 note 299).

39. Hannah maintains that Jung deeply loved both women and both women loved him. Emma Jung even said years later: "'You see, he never took anything from me to give to Toni, but the more he gave her, the more he seemed to be able to give me.'" Toni Wolff overcame her jealousy and "realized later that Jung's unswerving loyalty to his marriage gave her more than she could possible have had without it." (Hannah 1991, p. 119, 120)

40. The voice came to Jung as he was writing out his fantasies in his *Black Books* probably in the autumn of 1913. (Shamdasani 2005, p. 95 note 291) It was the voice of Maria Moltzer who was a wealthy heiress and Dutch doctor whom Jung met when she was an assistant at Burgholzli. (Bear 2003, p. 192, 291) Jung said she was "a patient, a talented psychopath who had a strong transference to me." (MDR, p. 185) She later set up an analytic practice. Bair comments:

> She was intense, intellectual, and driven, and Jung was so physically attracted to her that he called her the first inspiration for his formulation of the anima...Whether he consummated this passion is not known, but his attraction was real and lasting throughout his life. (Bair 2003, p. 192)

Moltzer was usually called "Sister Moltzer" and was described as being "Nunlike, ascetic, virginal and pure." (Bair 2003, p. 192) One aspect of Jung's anima had nun-like qualities. The Chinese characters he carved on a stone dedicated to Toni Wolff after her death read, "Lotus. Nun. Mysterious." (p. 559)

41. Buddhists speak of thoughts without a thinker. (Epstein 1995) They strive to achieve a state of consciousness that gets beneath and behind thoughts and sensations, a position not dissimilar to that of Hermes as described in volume 3. An aspect of the "natural mind" of the Tao can

be described as an objective consciousness beneath (behind) thoughts. Thoughts can be imagined as forms presented to us by the Mind, not our *personal* ego productions or confused with the Self that produced them.

Using the Self and the organism as similar archetypal constructs and the concept of nested selves (volume 1, Appendix C: Self and Organism), the Mind could be imagined as presenting species-specific forms and patterns with the feeling and perceptual forms in a dog, for example, being significantly different from humans.

42. A sense that active imagination is working is when unexpected things happen as the plot and characters begin to take on a life of their own. This can lead to an *auseinandersetzung*—a having it out between the conscious and unconscious positions covering all aspects of a conflict "always with a hint of eventually coming to terms." (Hannah 1991, p. 109) Jung learned to press the figures he

> encountered in his imagination until they told him what they wanted of him or told him why they appeared to him. (p.115)

Broadly speaking, Jung's psychotherapeutic method is active imagination: "opening to the unconscious and giving free rein to fantasy, while at the same time maintaining a conscious viewpoint." (Chodorow 1991, p. 34) Jung understood the therapeutic value of artistic expression:

> Jung's work gave credence to the use of art as a means by which the patient could become an object to himself...The creative act evokes material that is available for analysis and is at the same time cathartic. By virtue of the non-literal or apparently non-rational aspect of the creative act, deep feelings that defy words can be symbolically represented. (C. Schmais, 1974, Dance Therapy in Perspective, *Dance Therapy: Focus on Dance VII*, K. Mason, ed., p. 7-12, American Association for Health, Physical Education and Recreation: Washington D. C. p. 9 quoted in Chodorow 1991, p. 34)

As early as 1916 Jung recognized expressive body movements as one "of numerous ways to give form to the unconscious." (CW 8, ¶ 167-171 referenced in Chodorow 1991, p.1) "[Jung] frequently relied on the symbolic meaning of unconscious motor phenomena to understand and communicate with patients who were extremely withdrawn."(CW 1, ¶ 82, referenced in Chodorow 1991, p. 45)

Dance/movement therapy with children provides a good illustration of the embodiment of the psyche through play that facilitates the transformation of emotions. Jungian analyst and dance therapist Joan Chodorow realized "that everything [children] did was a mirroring of the world in movement: while they were watching something, they would imitate it. When they remembered something, they enacted the memory...Children learned about the world and about themselves through their bodies." (Chodorow 1991, p. 12):

> All of the arts—dance, painting, clay, dress-up—were seen as many languages through which the children could express and interpret their experiences...The process we call child development is completely interwoven with the creative process. (p. 13)

> It is important to remember that the earliest experience we have of consciousness is through the body. Physical consciousness is the foundation from which we continue to develop psychologically...Judith Hubback reflects... "Patients who live well in their bodies produce images which develop into symbols much more readily than those who do not appreciate themselves as physical beings." (J. Hubback, 1988, *People Who do Things to Each Other: Essays in Analytical Psychology*, Chiron Publications: Wilmette, Illinois, p. 26 quoted in Chodorow 1991, p. 37, 38)

Dance/movement therapy emphasizes being embodied, being in the body. Our emotional states and emotional histories are stored in the body. Chodorow writes, "It is as if certain memories are stored kinesthetically and can best be retrieved through the movements of the body." (Chodorow 1991, p. 115) Dance therapy uses movement and body experience to express and transform emotions, with the analyst serving as witness and container. Jung emphasized the importance of grounding the symbolic in the body:

> When the great swing has taken an individual into the world of symbolic mysteries, nothing comes of it, nothing *can* come from it, unless it has been associated with the earth, unless it has happened when that individual was in the body...And so individuation can only take place if you first return to the body, to your earth, only then does it become true. (Jung 1976b, vol. 2, p. 473 quoted in Chodorow 1991, p. 152)

When engaged in dance therapy, the participant has to stay with the image for the movement to be authentic:

> If the mover can stay focused on the body part or symptom as it is, without trying to change it, the process of denial and repression may be reversed. A meaningful symbolic gesture may emerge along with feelings associated with

the complex. When this happens, we see a symbol in the process of transformation, as it moves out of the personal unconscious and into an expressive form that is bearable and can be consciously understood. (Chodorow 1991, p. 122)

Eliade wrote: "Life cannot be *repaired*, it can only be *recreated*." (M. Eliade, 1975, *Myth and Reality,* Harper and Row: New York, p. 30 quoted in Chodorow 1991, p. 107) Chodorow adds, "In analysis, active imagination is that re-creative process. Dance/movement is one of its forms." (Chodorow 1991, p. 107) Within the relationship between mover/ analysand and a witness/analyst, "the mover may begin to internalize the reflective function of the witness, i.e., to yield to the unconscious stream of bodily felt sensations and images, while at the same time bringing the experience into conscious awareness." (p. 113)

"Symbolic play activates the image producing function of the psyche (i.e., the imagination) which puts us in touch with ourselves." (Chodorow 1991, p. 104) "A self-directed, imaginative movement process takes people directly to the deepest affects," Chodorow writes, leading to an emotional catharsis and a reversal of the process of denial and aggression. (p. 36) Containment is often necessary to move through the most intense emotional onslaughts and emerge with spontaneous insight and new integration:

> To contain is to feel deeply what is in us, bear the terrible discomfort, and find a way to express it symbolically. Symbolic expression holds the tension of the opposites. We feel the full impact while at the same time maintaining a bit of observing ego. Development occurs when we contain the affect, the therapeutic relationship is at once container and process. (p. 37)

See note 77 in volume 1, chapter 2 for more on active imagination.

43. Von Franz states that any unconscious content can be projected, projection being the involuntary expulsion of subjective contents into a person or an object. It is the tendency to see peculiarities and ways of behaving in others that we ourselves display without being aware of it. Whenever excessive emotional fascination is involved, projection is active. (von Franz 1975, p. 77, 78)

The first stage of projection is simply archaic identity—projection is seen as if it were the perception of reality. (von Franz 1975, p. 79) Only when a "superstition" is outlived is it a projection. Projection can be more narrowly restricted to the time when the need arises to dissolve the "identity" with the object because it has become a disturbing factor—it hinders adaptation. (CW 6, ¶ 783) Withdrawal of the projection is necessary because the conscious view is fanatically being defended while there are doubts of the rightness of one's own view.

(von Franz 1975, p. 78) The last stage of working with a projection is recognizing the image as a psychic content that originally belonged to one's own personality. (p. 79)

It involves considerable moral effort to withdraw projections, including all scientific and religious doctrines. Projections must be seen as a psychic rather than concrete "outer." (von Franz 1975, p. 78) "Is not our entire picture of the world a projection?" von Franz asks, and compares this concept to ideas in Hinduism and Leibniz' "'windowless' monads." (p. 79)

One must remember that it usually takes "real" world objects and interactions to activate and give "form" to archetypal potentials within, or, in dynamic systems theory terms, to bring about the emergence of the archetypal dimension of human experience. We are part of, and participate in, archetypal forces without and within; we are unique, time-bound, and (potentially) conscious expressions of these forces. (see note 41)

For the different levels of relationship to the anima and animus from the physical to the spiritual, see von Franz in Jung 1964, p. 185, 186, 194, 195 and Appendix G: The Sacred Prostitute and the Erotic Feminine in volume 3 of *The Dairy Farmer's Guide*.

44. Barbara Hannah, who knew Jung well, maintained that Jung's withdrawing of anima projections "enabled him to see his women patients as they really were and is the secret of his unparalleled genius as an analyst." (Hannah 1991, p. 125)

45. Von Franz said of Jung:

> The feminine factor had a determining influence on Jung's personality and thought. The intellect, the purely masculine spirit of the world of professional scholarship, was alien to him, because this world knows nothing of the process of fertilization through the unconscious. "But a larger mind bears the stamp of the feminine; it is endowed with a receptive and fruitful womb which can reshape what is strange and give it a familiar form." That is the "rare gift of a maternal intellect [Jung's remarks about Richard Wilhelm in CW 15, ¶ 76]," which was characteristic of Jung. (von Franz 1975, p. 145)

46. Jung's practice was doing well in 1914, with clients coming from Europe as well as the United States and Great Britain. (Bair 2003, p. 253)

47. Many youth in the 1960s "tripped" into the depths of the unconscious using LSD and some had terrifying "bummer trips" that triggered a psychosis. LSD experiments were conducted in the 1950's as a way to study psychotic processes and the CIA was interested in using it as a truth serum. Ken Kesey, who wrote *One Flew Over the Cuckoo's Nest*, was unwittingly exposed to LSD as an undergraduate at Stanford in a

CIA-sponsored psychology experiment. Professors Richard Alpert and Timothy Leary of Harvard were fired for their use of LSD that began in the late 1950's. Alpert became a devote of a Hindu guru and changed his name to Ram Dass, becoming a leading spokesperson for "New Age" spirituality since the late 1960s.

Many tribes in Central and South America use powerful hallucinogens to introduce people to the psychic depths in a ritually controlled and sacred manner. Shamans are the most revered members of indigenous tribes because, for various reasons, they are able to make the treacherous journey into the depths of the psyche, thereby coming in contact with the spirits they will work with to aid their tribes. The shaman ("medicine man") is the model of a conscious, individuated person who can relate to the psychic depths and is the cultural antecedent of modern psychotherapists. Von Franz writes, "The symbolic inner experiences which the shaman lives through during his period of initiation *are identical with the symbolic experiences the man of today lives through during the individuation process.*" (von Franz 1975, p. 263) Egotistical shamans, like egotistical psychologists, can abuse this power for personal gain or sense of importance. Anyone who gets close to the source will attract a following with the manna personality that develops, be they Jung or Charles Manson.

48. Jung's *Black Books* shows that the day of the hauntings was January 30, 1916, not the summer of 1916 as Bair stated. (Shamdasani 2005, p. 101)

49. Hannah explains that "parapsychological phenomena often take place when there is something in the unconscious that is striving, as it were, to become conscious." This is true with poltergeist phenomena in adolescents "who have not yet become conscious of the great change that is taking place in them." (Hannah 1991, p. 121) An example is Jung's cousin about whom he wrote his doctoral thesis.

50. A woman friend said, "[Emma] tried very hard to accept and understand [Jung's relationship with Toni Wolff], but it was so bewildering, so impossible really." (Bair 2003, p. 265, 266) Emma may have "grudgingly accepted [Toni] as part of Jung's ongoing self-analysis." (p. 388) Living within the rigid Swiss social structure, she did not want to embarrass her wealthy family or the distinguished Wolff family. She kept her anger to herself and tried to keep the affair from being publicly known. (p. 265-267) "[Emma] was ever loyal and had accepted his mistress with grace and dignity beyond description." (p. 314) Being married to an analyst isolated her from Swiss society, and she could not talk to any of Jung's colleagues about her problems. (p. 250, 251)

A close friend of Toni Wolff's believed an "'exceptional relationship'" developed among the three only "because of the 'quality of the three persons involved...it was very different from an 'affair'...There was responsibility, and a common task which was beyond but which included a love relationship.'" (Bair 2003, p. 267) Dr. Joseph Henderson believed:

> As nearly as possible in our monogamous society, Jung found two wives in these women and so provides no model for the rest of us to follow. It depended on a form of consciousness that totally transcended the ordinary worldly model—that of an important man who maintains a marriage and indulges himself on the side with a mistress. ("C. G. Jung, Emma Jung, and Toni Wolff," in Jensen, ed., 1982, *C. G. Jung, Emma Jung, and Toni Wolff*, The Analytical Psychology Club of San Francisco: San Francisco, quoted in Bair 2003, p. 738 note 73)

When Ruth Bailey, who became a close friend of the Jungs, first met Emma in 1926 she said "sad" was the only word to describe Jung's marriage and she saw "a deep sadness" in Emma's eyes. (Bair 2003, p. 355, 356) The relationship was difficult for Jung's children, especially Jung's son, growing up in a constrained, wealthy Swiss community. (p. 319)

51. "The *Red Book* is at the center of Jung's life and work," states Jungian scholar Sonu Shamdasani. Jung stopped working in it as he began his serious study of alchemy around 1930. Jung said that alchemy, starting with his reading of *The Secret of the Golden Flower* in 1928, allowed the contents of the *Red Book* to find "their way into reality." (Shamdasani 2005, p. 102, 103)

52. The Lakota Sioux and many other tribes tried to replicate on earth what they saw in the circle of the stars. They aligned their lives with star arrangements and movements by using star-based calendars. This told them where to migrate and where to set up camps in relation to a center of the world, that being Bear Butte, South Dakota for the Lakota. The center is chosen or "found" because the symbolism of that particular spot "reflects" the symbolism seen in the stars. The circle is one of the Lakota's most sacred concepts, with the circle of heaven being replicated in the circle of teepees in a Lakota campsite and the individual family circle being contained within the circular base of the tipi—"As above, so below." (Goodman 1990)

    The circle was part of the sacred geometry developed by the Greek Pythagoras around 500 BCE. We teach geometry in high school, omitting the sacred dimension considered central to the Pythagoreans. (see Robert Lawlor, 1982, *Sacred Geometry: Philosophy and Practice*, Thames and Hudson: London)

53. The genesis of Jung's myth of modern man occurred on the Athi Plains in East Africa, nearly two years before. This is discussed later in the chapter.

54. In the terms of dynamic systems theory, the experience of every individual is a virtual reality. It is a unique expression in symbolic form of the stable attractors known as the cultural mimes, the stable psychological elements of the individual, and the individual's human physiology and morphology that transits through phase states known as human development. See volume 3, Appendix B: Bootstrapping the Archetypes, Appendix D: Dynamic Systems Theory and Human Development, and Appendix C: The Human as an Embodied Robot.

55. Magnolias are remarkable for their large showy blossoms that precede the appearance of the leaves in the spring. The flowers seem to come out of nowhere, emerging before a vegetative base is established to support the flowers by the food sugars generated in the leaves. This conveys a sense that spirit precedes the physical matrix, suggesting that material reality is generated, inspired, formed, and led by the spirit.

56. Herbert Schroeder, a research social scientist with the USDA Forest Service, has published several articles on the spiritual values of forests and trees. He presents an excellent example of the Eastern White Pine as a cultural Self symbol for the Iroquois League in Schroeder 1992.

57. The central image in Jung's Liverpool dream bears a remarkable similarity to a key motif in the great vision of the Sioux holy man Black Elk who grew up on the Great Plaines of America. In 1874, a year before Jung was born, a severely ill nine-year-old Black Elk had a vision that lasted for 12 days. (Neihardt 1972, p. 20-47) A prominent feature of the vision was circles divided into 4 parts, like a medicine wheel—a cross within a circle. (see Appendix B: The Mandala) The four points where the cross touches the perimeter of the circle of the medicine wheel are related to the four directions, which offer a basic differentiation of an originally chaotic cosmos (see volume 4, chapter 2 of *The Dairy Farmer's Guide*). Finding direction in a chaotic cosmos is analogous to finding a direction and therefore a path with meaning in one's life.

Towards the end of Black Elk's vision, he saw a flowering tree growing in the center of a vast circle composed of the individual hoops/circles of all nations. (Neihardt 1972, p. 43) The individual hoop/circle would be analogous to the city square in each quadrant in Jung's dream. In his vision, Black Elk was on Harney Peak in the Black Hills of South Dakota when he saw the flowering tree, but he said when explaining the vision, "But anywhere is the center of the world," (p. 43 note 8) echoing the saying in Hermetic philosophy and Christian mysticism: "God is a spiritual sphere (or circle) whose center is everywhere and whose periphery is nowhere." (see Appendix B: the Mandala)

In the Native American pipe ceremony, when the pipe is loaded, it and the pipe bearer become the sacred center of the universe and everything becomes relevant to that position in an Einsteinian sense of the observer.

58. Jung developed a friendship with Wilhelm who was a masterful German scholar of ancient Chinese texts. Jung wrote the forward to Wilhelm's

translation of *I Ching*, still one of the best translations. Wilhelm noted "remarkable parallels between Jung's ideas and those of the Chinese sages...[believing] that both descended to the depths of the collective psyche where they encountered the same states of being, and their agreement demonstrated the essential truth of their conceptions." (Shamdasani 2005, p. 32, 33 note 84) The *I Ching* can be helpful in developing a symbolic relationship with the seasons as I describe in volume 4, chapter 2 of *The Dairy Farmer's Guide*.

Barbara Hannah explains that much of *The Secret of the Golden Flower* relates to the lowest levels of the human psyche where the most profound realizations come from. These realizations are the same in the East and the West. Humans are alike at their deepest levels, what Jung called the central fire, animal soul level, and primeval ancestor levels. (Hannah 1991, p. 17, 190; fig. 1, p. 35 in volume 1 of *The Dairy Farmer's Guide*)

Jung cautioned against imitation—wholesale adoption of beliefs and practices from other cultures, when one gets above the primal ancestor level and into the large cultural groupings like East and West. (Hannah 1991, p. 190, 242) One senses something alien in another culture at the higher levels beginning with the more differentiated cultural characteristics of the collective unconscious. Insights into another culture from these levels are "by no means entirely the same, similar, or even comparable to [one's] own psychic experiences" as Jung noted from his experiences in India. (p. 242) Jung believed one cannot adopt the realizations from these cultures "without doing violence to the structure of our own inheritance." (p. 190)

59. Unlike Freud, Jung did not seek to humiliate and ostracize opponents, but remained on friendly terms with some of them (Bair 2003, p. 282, 283):

> Freud seldom refined or departed from views he generally expressed once; he held them forever, whereas Jung maintained a lifelong openness to new ideas and new ways of thinking... Jung welcomed the new, just as long as he originated it; he was unafraid to change or refine a position, or to admit he had been in error, but only if he made the admission first; he permitted dialogue and dissension, but only if he was the ultimate arbiter. (p. 552, 553)

Like Freud, Jung was often overbearing in asserting his viewpoint. He could be "juvenile, aggressive, and unfair" in interchanges (Bair 2003, p. 279), treating opponents spitefully and sarcastically in a master/pupil manner in response to perceived criticism and honest disagreement. (p. 280) He barreled along on his own path, reluctant to acknowledge others who had developed similar ideas or giving credit to those who helped him develop his ideas. (p. 282) On the positive side, "to the end of his life, he possessed an almost childlike wonder as 'one book opened another' within his consistently evolving system." (p. 553)

60. Jung was critical of science and the scientific method and believed that every field of human endeavor was relevant to psychology because psychology studies the nature of the human, "the doer of the deed." (Shamdasani 2003, p. 18; CW 10, ¶ 498; CW 8, ¶ 421-423) Only psychology "could grasp the subjective factor that underlay other sciences," therefore psychology was "the fundamental scientific discipline." (Shamdasani 2003, p. 15) A major problem in attempting to synthesize knowledge and achieve a holistic base is specialization in the sciences that led "to a narrowing of the horizon and inbreeding" and an enormous amount of details. (p. 20, 21)

Jungian psychology has generally been dismissed by academic psychology because, as Jungian scholar Sonu Shamdasani noted, "from the 1920's onward, it was generally held that the use of experimentation and statistical methods formed the crucial traits that ensured the scientific status of psychology." (Shamdasani 2003, p. 29, 30)

Jung criticized the artificial limitations of experimentation in his 1952 paper on synchronicity. (CW 8, ¶ 821, 864) The experimental method consists of formulating definite questions thereupon forcing nature to orient its answer to them, preventing nature from "answering out of the fullness of her possibilities." (¶ 864) The types of questions posed delimit the answers obtained. Extraneous events are excluded as well as unique and rare events. Biology can handle unique specimens by having different individuals view them, but psychology is plagued with only a memory of ephemeral events and are therefore outside the purview of empirical science. Jung believed the ephemeral events are not to be discarded if "there was a sufficient number of reliable individual observations." (CW 8, ¶ 821)

In medical psychology, the object/patient poses the questions to the doctor—nature experiments with the doctor and expects an answer, unlike experimental psychology where the experimenter freely chooses the questions to be posed. (CW 10, ¶ 532) Jung said, "He who wants to get to know the human soul will find out next to nothing from experimental psychology." He recommended that one "hang up exact science and put away the scholar's gown, to say farewell to his study and wander with human heart through the world...[and] experience love, hate and passion in every form in one's body." (CW 7, ¶ 409, translation modified in Shamdasani 2003, p. 63)

Jung said his work was empirically based. (Feb. 9, 1951, Library of Congress, Wash. D.C. referenced in Shamdasani 2003, p. 167) He did not limit his concept of scientific proof to what he called the Anglo-Saxon definition: "an explanation of phenomena capable of being checked and observed by others and found to possess an unchanging and predictable order." (E. Bennett, 1961. *C. G. Jung*, Barrie and Rockliff: London, p. 99 quoted in Shamdasani 2003, p. 98) Jung felt the usual definition of scientific proof was more analogous to chemical or physical proof. He pointed out that evidence is commensurable to the area of investigation and the way of proving a fact varies with the discipline. "The question ought to be formulated: what is physical, biological, psychological, legal and philosophical evidence?" (Jung 1976a, p. 565) Jung said he followed the scientific method: "I observe, I classify, I establish relations and sequences between the observed data, and I even show the possibility of prediction." (p. 567) Like every scientific theory, Jung said his theories met the criteria of being a principle of understanding and a way of explaining and interpreting events. (p. 562)

Jung knew, of course, there is a link between psyche and the body, but for several reasons he was apprehensive about emphasizing that link in his consideration of the collective unconscious and other phenomena. He was fearful this would maintain the reductionist approach to psychology that Freud had begun. It finds its ultimate expression in psychopharamacology that now dominates psychiatry. (J. Acocella, 2000, "The empty couch: what is lost when psychiatry turns to drugs?" *The New Yorker*, May 8, 2000, p. 112-118) The belief is that humans are simply the sum of their chemical reactions and psychological problems are a consequence of chemical imbalances that can be remedied with the appropriate pill(s).

Jung felt we knew far too little about the psyche and about matter to be making links between them. (CW 3, ¶ 424) The phenomena coming out of the psyche must always be the beginning and ending "facts" we work with. (¶¶ 405, 388-424) Linking one's "proofs" to physics and chemistry is problematic because what are considered to be facts and theories change.

Jung did not imply that only the psychic exists, but simply that we cannot see beyond the psychic. (MDR, p. 351) We know that archetypes are real because the effects that have on us, but we do not know the real nature of archetypes or the psyche. "All comprehension and all that is comprehended is in itself psychic, and to that extent we are hopelessly cooped up in an exclusively psychic world." (p. 352)

Jung recognized the importance of developing models as long as we don't forget they are maps and not the territory. He was always open to new ways of conceptualizing and approaching the psyche, and had in-depth discussions with Wolfgang Pauli, one of the most prominent nuclear physicists ever, about the relationship between psychology and nuclear physics. "Thank God I'm Jung and not a Jungian," he said, unlike von Franz who has been described as attempting to preserve Jungian psychology by fossilizing it. Dynamic systems theory and situated robotics offer new ways to reformulate the concepts of archetypes and the collective unconscious. (see Appendices A-F in volume 3 of *The Dairy Farmer's Guide*)

Entering Jungian psychology as I did as a scientist, I have been sensitive to anti-scientific bias and unscientific thinking within the Jungian community. I presented my observations in an article, "Jungian Psychology and Science—A Strained Relationship," (Merritt 1988) to be reprinted in *A Jungian Bouquet* (in preparation).

61. Many famous artists and writers analyzed with Jung, including Herman Hesse and Elizabeth Shipley Sergeant. He developed a long list of devoted and impressive women followers, particularly in the English speaking world, including Mary Ester Harding and the daughter of John D. Rockefeller. (Bair 2003, p. 267, 268, 300-307)

62. One can compare Jung's lifetime of development and elaboration of his *prima materia* experience to the Sioux Holy Man Black Elk who did many vision quests and made it a life task to understand and enact the elements of the great vision he had in his childhood. (see DeMaille 1984 and Neihardt 1972)

63. The Gnostics had confronted the primal world of the unconscious but there were not enough accounts at the time for Jung to know how the Gnostics understood their images. "[Their] systems consist only in small part of immediate psychic experiences, the greater part being speculative and systematizing recensions," Jung wrote, plus there was a huge time gap between the Gnostics and the present. (CW 13, p. 3)

64. Jung's study of alchemy was anticipated by a series of dreams around 1926 about a strange wing or annex to his house that he sensed was always there. He wondered why he didn't know what was in it. In a dream where he finally entered the wing, he discovered a wonderful library he later came to realize was an alchemical library—much like the one he eventually assembled for himself. The unknown wing represented an aspect of himself he was not yet conscious of. (MDR, p. 202-204)

65. Jung had particular difficulty relating to men. "Many of Jung's friendships with men deteriorated after mutual jousting for intellectual supremacy," Bair writes (Bair 2003, p. 748 note 17), beginning well and ended badly "in bitterness, rejection, and recrimination." (p. 71) The lasting affect of the sexual abuse from the priest was that Jung found it "downright disgusting" that any man tried to develop an "intimate relationship" with him (in a platonic sense). (p. 71, 72)

Hans Schmid, once a personal and professional friend of Jung, accused him of being unable to love in three important ways: in his profession, in the reactions of people close to him, especially Toni and Emma, and in his reaction to Hans. (Bair 2003, p. 281, 282) He told Jung he thought of him like this:

> In a tower at the Obersee you...have adopted the heritage of Nietzsche, a father to no one, a friend to no one, completely self-sufficient, fulfilled by yourself. Across the way, here

> and there, live a few other male and female introverts, each in his own tower, loving humanity in those "farthest away," thus protecting themselves from the devilish love of their "neighbors." (p. 283)

Jung's difficulties in the realm of intimacies and relationships could be attributed to a deep Eros wound. Attachment theorists would associate the origin of his wound to a disturbed connection with his depressed, hysterical, ghost-fearing mother whom Jung felt had abandoned him when she was hospitalized during his infancy. The deep conflict in his parent's marriage and the sexual abuse were other contributing factors.

I propose that his Eros wound led him to emphasize the dark side of God that he saw as necessary to compensate for what he perceived to be too much light in Christianity. Because of this wound Jung was unable to adequately convey the vital role of love and intimacy essential for becoming a whole human being. He could not fully relate to the essence of Christianity's message—God is love, but rather to a God of awesome power, irrational circumstance, and the dazzling realm of nature *devoid of humans*—a world of divine beauty and stark cruelty. Jung's intimacy problem can be put into an archetypal framework and returned to Jung's system because of its broad, flexible and inclusive structure. Namely, the lacuna in Jung's psyche and system can be addressed by incorporating the archetype of a foundational and sustaining love: the loving, mothering side of the Great Goddess. (see Appendix G: Jung's Eros Wound and his Image of God)

66. Two books by Fred Gustafson explore the Black Madonna as the repressed feminine: *The Black Madonna* (2008, Daimon Verlag: Einsiedeln, Switzerland) and *The Moonlit Path: Reflections on the Dark Feminine* (ed., 2003, Nicolas-Hays: Berwick, ME).

67. Jung's alchemical studies turned him away from individual analysis and patient histories as a means of evolving theory and towards general psychic problems and historical correspondences—the archetypes of the collective unconscious. (Bair 2003, p. 358, 377, 395) An archetypal approach helps absolve the arbitrariness of using case histories.

68. The earliest existing alchemical writings, known as gnostic, are of late Greek-Egyptian origin (an aspect of Jung's Philemon). Writers like Zosimos (third century AD) were called Christian gnostic natural philosophers. (von Franz 1975, p. 199)

69. A Platonic Scholastic, William of Conches (1080-1154), had a conception of a world soul that permeates the universe. For Conches, the chief source of all knowledge of nature possessed by humans and animals was a hypothetical *sensus naturae*—"an unconscious, instinctive, supernatural knowledge" associated with the Holy Ghost. (von Franz 1975, p. 31) It enabled humans, animals and other living things to foretell the future. Many Scholastics and most Western alchemists expounded

this belief. The 16th century Swiss doctor and alchemist, Paracelsus, said man was a "prophet of the natural light" that is in one's "inward body" and "is always truthful" (p. 32) (similar to the "natural mind" of Jung's mother). One "learns" the *lumen naturae* through dreams and other forms of communication. (CW 8, ¶ 391) A dream of Descartes also revealed a belief in a natural light. (von Franz 1975, p. 32 note 57)

70. "[Goethe] regarded his *Faust* as an *opus magnum* or *divinum*. He called it his 'main business,' and his whole life was enacted within the framework of this drama," Jung noted. (MDR, p. 206) Von Franz commented that the Hermetic ideas of alchemy "formed Goethe's 'private religion,' which he took care to conceal but from which he received his deepest and greatest inspiration." (von Franz 1975, p. 35)

71. Jung's alchemical studies marked a shift in his intellectual, and to some extent his confidential, relationship with Toni Wolff—and it came at Wolff's own hands. Wolff feared Jung was abandoning orthodox medical and clinical psychology in his pursuit of what she perceived to be esoteric scholarship in alchemy that was pseudoscience at best, quackery at worst. (Bair 2003, p. 395) She feared Jung's interest in alchemy "would marginalize him within the medical-psychological community and lead to ridicule and scorn in the world at large." (p. 399)

In 1933 Wolff invited a group of interesting university students to meet Jung at his retreat in Bollingen, hoping that a discussion of new, trendy topics would divert Jung from his preoccupation with alchemy. In that group of students was an 18 year-old girl of "ferocious intelligence and fearless outspokenness" named Marie-Louise von Franz. (Bair 2003, p. 368) Von Franz immediately had "'a terrific transference and a big schoolgirl crush'" on Jung. (p. 369) Jung later put her to work utilizing her genius for picking out "symbolically interesting" material while foraging in the libraries. (p. 370) She was "an extraordinarily diligent researcher" and "trained herself to become expert in deciphering esoteric Medieval Latin handwritings and then translated the obscure texts into contemporary German, thus saving Jung literally years of labor." (p. 475)

Von Franz devoted her life to Jung and his psychology. She proudly stated, "intellectually, I replaced Toni Wolff in Jung's life," and gained Jung's confidence because Wolff, as von Franz saw it, "'was too much a slightly conventional Christian, and she refused to follow him'" in his interest in alchemy. (Bair 2003, p. 371) Von Franz worked closely with Jung throughout his life, becoming one of the leading Jungian analysts and the only woman "whose intellectual acumen Jung respected." (p. 555)

Jung said of Toni's refusal to follow him in his interest in alchemy: "All of a sudden Toni Wolff went out of my life just as fast as she came in. All of a sudden, that was the end." (Baer 2003, p. 390) (see Appendix G) Toni had a life-long devotion to the cause of analytical psychology, becoming a fine analyst and integral part of the Zurich Jungian scene.

72. The historic role of religions has been to create a spiritual and psychological standpoint to cope with the inevitable circumstances of life and
to offer humankind something more than the merely material conditions of existence. Von Franz writes:

> Only from a religious standpoint can an individual freely
> make judgments and decisions...But most religions have
> compromised with the world and with the State to such
> an extent that they have become creeds, that is, collective
> institutions with general convictions instead of a subjec-
> tive revelation of the irrational inner powers. Only the
> later can guarantee truly ethical behavior, while ethics
> without individual responsibility before God is simply
> conventional morality. (von Franz 1975, p. 260)

Religions have become part of a collective too closely aligned with the
state and the status quo. (p. 260, 261) Gone is Dietrich Bonhoeffer's
steep cost of discipleship (D. Bonhoeffer, 1953, *Letters and Papers from
Prison*, Eberhard Bethge, ed., Reginald Fuller, trans. Macmillan: NY;
1959/1995, *The Cost of Discipleship*, Simon & Schuster: NY) that would
see God's face in the inner city young black male who is behind bars,
in the infants with fetal alcohol syndrome, and in the Muslim suicide
bomber. The church restricts the boundless creativity and freedom of
God with dogmas and pat interpretations. Jung never forgot his childhood vision of God defecating on the church, demonstrating that God
was above dogmas, human constructs and scientific principles. Jung
believed Christianity has lost the focus of its originator on the ultimate
sanctity and freedom of the individual soul. (MDR, p. 212; CW 10, ¶
529, 536) "Are not Jesus and Paul prototypes of those who, trusting
their inner experience, have gone their individual ways in defiance of
the world?" Jung asks. (CW 10, ¶ 536)

The church has suppressed the symbol formation activity of the
unconscious as experienced by individuals, and church authority has
replaced the "natural" authority of the more conscious individual. Von
Franz points out, "*The individuation process, however, is incompatible with
any sort of social power claim...*[or]...a person pretend[ing] to be a well-
meaning, moderate liberal leader or a 'fatherly shepherd of souls.'" The
danger of having a minister or priest being a "shepherd of souls" is that
church members become dependent and can just as easily be willing to
follow destructive authority. (von Franz 1975, p. 263) Jung reproached
Protestantism for not extending their theological development "to the
point where the individual would take up the whole burden of responsibility for his inner life." (p. 263, 264) This is the only way the "inner
man," the Anthropos, can be found, a figure "similar to the Christ
figure but not identical with it [Appendix I]," giving one autonomy
with respect to dogma and the collective. "This inner Anthropos will

never play the game of 'sheep and shepherd,' 'because he has enough to do to be a shepherd to himself [CW14, ¶ 491].'" (p. 264)

Results from an extensive study at Baylor University published in 2006 revealed that 31.4% of American believers see God as an authoritarian figure responsible for global events like hurricanes and economic downturns. He is an angry, punitive God deeply involved in people's daily lives. Another 16% believe in a critical but distant God whose displeasure will be felt in the afterlife. There are 23% who believe in a benevolent God acting as a positive force in the world who is less likely to condemn and punish individuals. About 24% believe in a distant God who set the world in motion but is not active in the world nor holds clear opinions about what happens here. These four types cut across denominational and non-denominational lines. (Baylor Institute for Studies of Religion, "American piety in the 21st century," Selected findings from The Baylor University Survey, September 2006, Baylor University: www.baylor.edu/content/services/document.php/33304. pdf (Retrieved June 10, 2011)

73. The Jung family coat of arms had modified Rosicrucian, or Masonic, elements of the cross and grapes with a uniting symbol between them of a gold star—the philosophers gold, the symbol of the goal of the alchemical process. Jung's grandfather, after whom he was named, was a leading Freemason in Basel.

74. With the interests of his scholarly studies anchored in the late nineteenth century, Jung's cultural ideal was the iconic figure of Faust. (Bair 2003, p. 398, 399) Bair states that Jung's deep engagement with cultural tradition ended

> [with] the close of the nineteenth century...After that, he was by choice almost totally ignorant of twentieth-century arts and letters, for he seldom read contemporary fiction and never read biography or nonfiction unless it covered topical subjects that interested him. His favored form of recreational reading were *crimi*...He never went to the theater, attended lectures only on psychological subjects, and avoided concerts like the plague. (p. 398)

75. The distinction between Logos and Eros is depicted by the archetypal images of Sol and Luna, sun and moon:

> The "mild light" of the moon...merges things together rather than separates them. It does not show up objects in all their pitiless discreteness and separateness, like the harsh, glaring light of day, but blends in a deceptive shimmer the near and the far, magically transforming little things into big things, high into low, softening all colour

into a bluish haze, and blending the nocturnal landscape
into an unsuspected unity. (CW 14, ¶ 223)

76. Analytical psychologist Frances Wickes also talked with Mountain Lake, reporting a conversation similar to one Jung recorded:

> How does the white man keep his partnership with a God who lives in a church or a far off heaven? An Indian must feel his God always near him—He stretches out his hand and his God fills it with warmth. Then he knows that his father is the Sun. Even at night, his god is there, living in the warmth of the fire that burns upon his hearth. (Wickes collection, Library of Congress, Washington, DC quoted in Shamdasani 2003, p. 326 note 91)

Rituals are a human response to the "overpowering influence of God" and also an attempt to activate and manipulate that power. Christians believe that "through certain rites or by prayer, or a morality pleasing to the Divinity" they can influence God. (MDR, p. 253) Ritual can be seen in dynamic systems theory constructs as an activity that facilitates transition into the transpersonal dimension of human experience and a means of navigating in that realm. (Merritt 2008)

77. Many Christian Native Americans see no conflict with their practice of Native American traditional ceremonies. Elmer Running, a Catholic Sundance leader and "interpreter," liked to say, "There is only one God." The Sundance, sweat lodge, and vision quest ceremonies are intimately connected with the earth and sacred local environments.

78.

> The foreign land assimilates its conqueror. But unlike the Latin conquerors of Central and South America, the North Americans preserved their European standards with the most rigid puritanism, though they could not prevent the souls of their Indian foes from becoming theirs. (CW 10, ¶ 103)

79. Jung described an objectivity trap in science and phenomenology, particularly in areas like anthropology, summarized by Sonu Shamdasani:

> The fear of subjectivity in scholarship led to thinking being forsaken in a quest for clear facts, and to the emphasis on amassing objective material records, the use of statistics, and photographic and phonographic registration. Presuppositionlessness had become an ideal—the assumption that "the material dictates and the thought orders itself under it." However, he argued that it was only a short step from this ideal to mindlessness. What was left out of this was

a consideration of the psychological factor of judgment, which was the "conditio sine qua non of knowledge." (Shamdasani 2003, p. 324)

80. The union of opposites in Jung engendered powerful transferences onto him. Barbara Hannah said she had the "strongest *sentiment du déjà vu* that I ever experienced" when she first met Jung. He was the most whole person she had ever seen (Hannah 1991, p. 191):

> Because the opposites were so much united in him, and he was by this time so whole, that more one-sided people were inevitably drawn to him to get at least a glimpse back into their own lost wholeness. It was, of course, a projection, but it was a fruitful projection, for that missing quality in themselves was often seen in him for the first time in adult life. (If it remained forever a projection, it naturally became regressive, but, in a successful outcome, it was gradually seen to be a projection, the projector thus becoming aware of his or her No. 2 personality for the first time.) (p. 196)

Hannah said of her own analysis with Jung, starting in 1931, and of the confrontation with his wholeness: "He let nothing through, and one was constantly challenged in one's most inferior and unconscious areas." (Hannah 1991, p. 201)

81. Jung felt that Buddhism was not a proper philosophy because it challenges man, whereas philosophy is a rather pure intellectual exercise needing "a good deal of intellectual free play, undisturbed by moral and human entanglements." "Small and fragmentary people" want to participate as well "without getting fatally involved in big issues far beyond their powers of endurance and accomplishment." They take the "long road" and may be upset by "the divine impatience of a genius...But after a few generations he will reassert himself by sheer force of numbers." (CW 10, ¶ 1006)

Thomas Berry describes different types of consciousness with a medieval story about the motivation of three stone carriers working on a cathedral. The first person says he is carrying stones—the life of physical labor; the second says he is supporting his family—the average family man; the third says, "he's building a cathedral." All are engaged in an important and valid activity but have different consciousnesses about what they are doing. Berry stated that in our troubled times "we need people who realize that we are shaping a new order of things." (Ryley 1998, p. 234, 235)

Jung suffered his own "divine impatience of a genius" that disturbed "small people in his environment," but he was very tolerant and accepting of every person because they were "at whatever level of consciousness it had to be lived." (Hannah 1991, p. 247) This was Jung's interpretation of the centers of the city quarters in relation to the magnolia tree at the very center of Liverpool in his Liverpool Self dream. (p. 186)

82. One may have a meaningful life and honor numinous experiences while relating to one's psyche and others in a conscious, holistic manner and not be connected with nature. Three additional elements are required: extended periods of being immersed in nature so it can impact the psyche, an absence of negative complexes about nature, and a psychological and intellectual framework together with an educational system that integrates the human experience from the intrapsychic through the galactic—a Jungian ecopsychology for example.

83. Jung used a question about karma to further explore the personal and individual in relationship to the archetypal realm and the quest for meaning. He referred to Buddha not answering whether karma is personal or impersonal. Jung said:

> What I feel to be the resultant of my ancestor's lives, or a karma acquired in a previous personal life, might perhaps equally well be an impersonal archetype which today presses hard on everyone and has taken a particular hold upon me—an archetype such as, for example, the development over the centuries of the divine triad and its confrontation with the feminine principle; or the still pending answer to the Gnostic question as to the origin of evil, or, to put it another way, the incompleteness of the Christian God-image. (MDR, p. 318)

Jung felt the meaning of his existence, his "suprapersonal task," was to answer the question life addressed to him, or, conversely that perhaps the question he addressed to the world and sought his own answer to was a question that preoccupied his ancestors that they were unable to answer.

84. Jung was totally exhausted by the India trip, suffering from a severe attack of amoebic dysentery, and sleeping poorly because of red images he associated with "the nature of evil as evidenced by the Goddess Kali." As he drifted in and out of drugged sleep during his hospitalization, he had dreams difficult to understand but all with the central theme of rescuing the Grail for Western culture. (Bair 2003, p. 428)

85. The iron gnome figure relates to a Medieval Celtic belief in gnomes, associated with creative phallic energy and Jung's experiences with the nightmare phallus/telesphorus/childhood manikin. Iron gnomes would personify the alchemist's sense of the spirit in nature's organic *and* inorganic realms. (see Appendix H: Jung's Phallic Self Image)

86. Bair gives a slightly different version of the dream, including an opening scene with Jung being about a thousand miles above India looking down toward a castle in Cornwall, England where the Holy Grail was

to be celebrated. This suggests that despite being in India his focus was elsewhere. (Bair 2003, p. 428, 429)

87. Jung had a shamanic experience as he was recovering from the worst of his illness. "He felt that his body had been dismembered and cut up into small pieces. Then, over quite a long period, it was slowly collected and put together again with the greatest care." (Hannah 1991, p. 283) There are many examples of shamans throughout the world who are initiated by having semi-divine beings or ancestors dismember their bodies before reassembling them with renewed internal organs and bones. Jung had the almost intolerable task of reassembling his body himself, again paralleling shamans whom Eliade described as being sick men who had succeeded in curing themselves. (Mircea Eliade, 1964, *Shamanism: Archaic Techniques of Ecstasy*, Willard R. Trash, trans., Bollingen Series LXXVI, Pantheon Books: New York, p. 27, 50 referenced in Hannah 1991, p. 283)

Even after his body was reassembled, "he first re-experienced his body as that of a big fish. This was such a realistic experience that for some time, whenever he was fed with spoonfuls of soup, he felt anxious about whether it would not flow out again at his gills!" (Hannah 1991, p. 284)

88. On his deathbed seventeen years later "he would emerge occasionally from a comatose state and, obviously referring to a vision, say something that sounded like 'how wonderful.'" (Bair 2003, p. 623)

89. Jung emerged from his near death experience with a profound sense of the eternal. He described the experience as being "the ecstasy of a non-temporal state in which present, past and future are one." (MDR, p. 295, 296) It is the feeling of "a sum, an iridescent whole, containing all at once expectation of a beginning, surprise at what is now happening, and satisfaction or disappointment with the result of what has happened. One is interwoven into an indescribable whole and yet observes it with complete objectivity." (p. 296)

He came to fully accept himself and "the conditions of existence," knowing that mistakes are part of the bargain. "There is no guarantee—not for single moment—that we will not fall into error or stumble into deadly peril," cautioning that, "Anyone who takes the sure road is as good as dead." (MDR, p. 297)

He learned that "one must accept the thoughts that go on within oneself of their own accord" and not suppress one's judgments either. (MDR, p. 298) It is also important to affirm one's destiny, which "forge[s] an ego that does not break down when incomprehensible things happen; an ego that endures, that endures the truth, and that is capable of coping with the world and with fate. Then, to experience defeat is also to experience victory." (p. 297)

After Jung's illness he emphasized even more than before "the necessity of always looking for the opposite in everything...even to his conviction that the individual is the only thing that matters." (Hannah 1991, p. 289)

90. See note 71.

91. Jung wanted the third part of *Mysterium Coniuncionis*, that von Franz wrote, to be published with his first two parts, originally intending to publish all three volumes under both names. (Hannah 1991, p. 230) Part three became *The Aurora Consurgens* published separately in the Bollingen Series under von Franz's name.

Von Franz positioned herself as the official explicator of Jung's psychology after he died, known to some as "'one of those who fossilize theories by a strict adherence to them.'" (Bair 2003, p. 368) Von Franz's view could be described as seeing Jung's psychology as being "'final and fixed at his death, and no subsequent interpretation of theory could or should be either superimposed upon or incorporated within it.'" (p. 770 note 69)

92. The paperback edition of *Answer to Job* became a best seller in the United States. (Hannah 1991, p. 304)

Jung deliberately tried to use equivocal, ambiguous language to do justice to the double aspect and paradoxical nature of the psyche. (Jung 1976a, p. 71) His writings contained logically understandable arguments *and* allowed a voice for the unconscious. (von Franz 1975, p. 4) Von Franz noted that this double aspect got lost in R. F. C. Hull's translation into English of the *Collected Works*. (p. 4 note 3)

93. The kingfisher has associations with Jung's Philemon who came to him in a dream early in his "confrontation with the unconscious" and to the fisher king of the Grail legend, a myth Jung considered to be of utmost importance to the West.

94. Jung's childhood experience with the stone signified an ability to identify with two different loci of consciousness.

95. Jung adds a word of caution to New Age spirituality that is always in danger of getting lost in its phantasms:

> Cut off the intermediary world of mythic imagination, and the mind falls prey to doctrinaire rigidities. On the other hand, too much traffic with these germs of myth is dangerous for weak and suggestible minds, for they are led to mistake vague intimations for substantial knowledge, and to hypostatize mere phantasms. (MDR, p. 316)

APPENDIX A

William Blake and the English Romantics

Ross Woodman, husband of Jungian analyst Marion Woodman, is a Blake scholar and authority on Milton, Shelley, and the Romantic poets. He called Jung the last Romantic, the Romantic who provided a theoretical framework for Romanticism. (Ryley 1998, p. 140) Woodman describes Romanticism as "a reaction against the triumph of Rationalism—of the Enlightenment in the eighteenth century. Above all, it is a reaction against the one-sided triumph of science and the scientific mind." (p. 135)

William Blake and the other Romantics were appalled by the environmental degradation and pollution becoming apparent in the early 19th century consequent to the emergent technological industrial "paradise." Their souls felt threatened by the rational attempt to control nature and a mechanical worldview that viewed nature as "a fixed order, governed by immutable laws...to which we must ultimately submit." What didn't fit this model was considered to be chaotic or demonic. (Ryley 1998, p. 137)

The Romantics rediscovered the unconscious in doing what the poet Keats called journeying into "some untravelled region of my mind" in a process he described as "soul making." (Ryley 1998, p. 137, 138) Blake, the father of Romanticism (p. 143) who perhaps put forth its most complete vision, considering Hell to be the objectified, "mathematically fixed space/time order of things which the Enlightenment thought of as Heaven...Hell was the energy we repressed in order to live conventionally." (p. 140) Heaven for Blake was the soul hiding in exile from the mechanical worldview, a soul participating in the creativity of nature. This soul was the opposite of Dante's medieval image of the soul identified with Reality itself, a reality created by God and identified with every movement of the vast cosmos. (p. 139)

The Romantics responded to Hell by indulging in what it excluded—feelings, the irrational, and the imaginative life oriented towards, and emerging out of, the sensuality of our own bodies and nature. The Romantic poets were preoccupied with giving shape and form to what they perceived to be the dynamism and creative operations of nature. They thought of the energy of nature as a life force operating through the imaginative capabilities of humans. This perpetually creates a second nature, a metaphorical body. The body is to be seen as "incarnated soul or soul in the process of its making," with a Romantic emphasis on process over product with the ideal always in the process of being made. They were referring to the human body as it is imaginatively perceived, imagination anchored in the sensuality and experience of the body; "the body as psyche rather than the body *opposed* to psyche." (Ryley 1998, p. 140, 141) The greater goal is the life of the imagination that enables us to inhabit what Jung calls psychic reality, Blake's *Jerusalem*, and the New Testament Kingdom of God that dwells within us. *Jerusalem* is about the psychic dynamics of building a conscious human body which Blake imagined as the spiritual, resurrected body of Christ. (p. 167-169) Every person has to build their own version of Jerusalem. (p. 178)

The Romantics struggled with accepting their feminine side and the repressed feminine in Western culture long associated with the body, sexuality, original sin, nature, and Satan. (Ryley 1998, p. 143) They used creative channels to release repressed energies, especially the powerful sexual energies, by locating them in the imaginal and metaphorical body. This gave form to the energies, transforming them in the process into an artistic metaphoric body—a poem, a painting, a song. (p. 141) Blake experienced himself as a fully resurrected body at one with the Risen Jesus, an imaginal construction achieved by writing his 1800's poem, *Milton*. Blake's Christ was Milton's feminine muse who dictated Milton's epic poem, *Paradise Lost*. It was a feminine and androgynous Christ, symbolic for Blake of the divine Inner Marriage of the masculine and feminine. (p. 141-146) Milton's epic, written in the 1660's, was his attempt to "'justify the ways of God to men' and to assert 'Eternal Providence.'" (Ryley 1998, p. 141, 142) It became a statement of Puritan belief that Woodman sees as bequeathing North America with "the trauma of sexuality that Puritans identified with original sin." (p. 147)

For Blake, repressing our powerful inner nature results in sickness: "Sooner murder an infant in its cradle than nurse unacted desires," he wrote. (Ryley 1998, p. 155) Repressed energy gathers strength and turns against us. We perceive it as being evil energy that could demolish us, for example, by succumbing to an irrational desire to visit brothels as an outlet for sexual desires. (p. 155, 156) The sexual energy of the brothel is of a driven nature because it is sexuality used to ward off the depression and despair of an imprisoned soul. (p. 157, 158) Blake believed sexual energy "belongs to [the] sacramental order of the imagination." When located and operating in the larger body—the imaginal and metaphorical body—it became "a hugely fulfilling part of one's life." (p. 158) (cf. the discussion of Gnostic alchemical sex in appendix H of volume 3)

Woodman believes this raw, unredeemed energy is "destructive because it has no creative social channel to flow into." (Ryley 1998, p. 156) "Blake's answer is that any person has the right and the responsibility to frame that [fearful] symmetry [of the tiger, from the 1794 poem, *The Tyger*], to release and shape his or her creativity, and restore the world to its original form." (p. 157) Blake's tiger and lamb lie down together in the New Jerusalem symbolic of the Inner Marriage of masculine (tiger) and feminine (lamb) energies to produce the goal—a conscious body, a body soul. (p. 159) Woodman associates archetypal feminine energy with the creative matrix to be celebrated by the disciplined archetypal masculine penetrating and channeling it into creative forms—an artifact, a film, a poem. It requires discipline to work with these archetypal forces without disrupting the unconscious or becoming crippled or paralyzed by it. (p. 160) This activity occurs in the soul-making space, the gap in Hermes' wand—the *viva-la-difference* space (see volume 3, chapter 8 of *The Dairy Farmer's Guide*). In Romantic love, Woodman asserts, the other person becomes the whole planet: "Conscious love has to be directed towards all Creation, not only towards each other." (p. 164) Hillman develops this idea by resurrecting the neo-platonic idea of Aphrodite as the Soul of the World (see Appendix K in volume 3), a sensuous world of allure and beauty.

Blake challenges us to come into our uniquely human form by bringing into consciousness, into a conscious human body, all other forms of Power that comprise the body—the mineral form of atomic cohesion, the vegetable form of cellular life, the animal form as biological reproduction. (Ryley 1998, p. 169) The Romantic vision is to be found in the "simple produce of the common day." Blake declared that the

New Jerusalem celebrated in the Book of Revelation was to be found in "'a Wild Flower' and 'a Grain of Sand.'" (p. 197)

Honoring the soul in nature means bringing consciousness to nature which does not happen automatically just by walking into a garden. As Woodman describes it:

> If I can quiet my own thinking and my own kinds of intrusive urgencies, I can gradually bring my thoughts into some kind of relationship with [nature]. I'll gradually begin to speak out of it, and it will begin to hear me. And I'll be enhanced, and it will be enhanced...The flowers will have the look of flowers that are looked at. There's a difference. (Ryley 1998, p. 172)

"Our rape of nature is our loathing of ourselves," Woodman writes. Blake believed we will not really know nature and will continue to pillage it until we become aware of our Divine nature and overcome our ignorance or our rejection of it. (Ryley 1998, p. 170, 173) Blake's creative process expressed through a poetry that enacts our creation, our union with the divine, can be seen as emergent phenomena in dynamic systems theory. In DST terms, our sense of divine origin emerges through conscious immersion in the human body and nature. This takes the full engagement of the human imagination, creativity, and the metaphor and symbol-creating ability of the psyche, resulting in the creation of the artistic artifacts—art, music, dance, stories, etc. This is full consciousness and *that* is what Romantics call the subtle body of the divine: the art is the body of the Divine.

Blake emphasized that we should enjoy the journey but it will be a struggle. (p. 169) We must arm ourselves with the healing powers of spiritual energies and engage in the ceaseless "Mental Fight" necessary to do the hard work. (Ryley 1998, p. 173) To make a genuine contribution and not generate more problems than we attempt to fix, we must be psychologically well grounded—we must know and forgive ourselves before we can know and forgive others. (p. 174) First we must understand what our enemy constellates in us:

> What does it mean to forgive the father? It means that I have absorbed that internalization of him in myself, and that I no longer need to act that out. I no longer need to project my father onto the world and do battle with him out there. Nor do I need to collude with the inner power principle he represents, and allow him to bully and victimize me in my own life. (p. 174)

This Romantic vision of the Reality of the "dreaming earth" is that death of the old is in service of new life. (Ryley 1998, p. 187) Shelley's "Ode to the West Wind" recognizes autumn's death as the potential spring of new development. We can learn to see and experience the seasons metaphorically, where the processes in nature are internal processes as well. (p. 185) Transformation through suffering is a feminine consciousness reflecting the death and rebirth aspects of nature. (p. 188) One doesn't heroically try to conquer death; one dies to be reborn in spirit and a more abundant life.

Blake called for a mutation of consciousness. The survival of our planet and the creation of a genuine global culture "requires a level of conscious understanding previously dreamt of only by visionaries but never actually achieved," declares Woodman. (Ryley 1998, p. 181) Jung's concept of the emerging New Age is that "we [are] moving into a new stage of psychic reality marked by the coming together of all the peoples of the Earth" (p. 191) as illustrated by his Liverpool dream. Blake's vision is of building a New Jerusalem that "is one city, one country, one humanity, one religion, one God. 'The Earth is one country, and humankind its citizens.'" (p. 192)

Woodman sees a mutation of consciousness arising through a cultivation of a sense of the reality of the body/soul, an ensouled, conscious body intertwined with a sense of the earth as a conscious body. *This* is the divine presence manifesting itself in planetary reality. In this vision, "the enlargement of the body as the form or container of the soul is the return of the feminine." (p. 195) The soul in the matter of the body and the planet *is* the Great Goddess, the archetypal feminine consciousness growing in Western consciousness. (Ryley 1998, p. 190, 191, 195, 196)

APPENDIX B

The Mandala

The mandala is a magic circle that functions as a symbol of the center and centering process in the psyche, and the Self as the totality of the psyche. The cosmic Anthropos and the mandala "both point to an ultimate inner psychic unity, to the Self," notes Marie-Louise von Franz. The mandala is also an "age-old symbol of the godhead and the cosmos." An early representation of Buddha was a twelve-spoked wheel and Christ was often represented in the center of a mandala with symbols of the four evangelists. (von Franz 1975, p. 141)

Von Franz describes how "a new image of the divine and of the ultimate structure of reality broke through into consciousness" during the genesis of Greek natural scientific thought in the seventh and sixth century BCE. The personal deities of the Greek pantheon were increasingly displaced by "the idea of an ultimate unitary ground of all being and of its circular or spherical structure, as well as its arrangement in accordance with its own internal laws." (von Franz 1975, p. 141, 142) Plato and later Plotinus clarified and developed ideas and imagery from earlier Greek philosophers (Mahnke 1966, p. 227 ff in von Franz 1975, p. 142):

> It was Plotinus, chiefly, who further expanded these representations and handed them on to the Christian era: the center of all being is the One, the light which radiates in all directions and into the infinite; this one is surrounded by the spherical covering of the world soul and further out, by the visible cosmos. But the center is the "spiritual sphere"... which is unity, wholeness and the godhead itself. (p. 142)

This god is "all-encompassing," and at the same time lives "inside in the depths" at the center point. (Mahnke 1966, p. 220 quoted in von Franz 1975, p. 143)

An image from Plotinus constantly appears in Hermetic philosophy and Christian mysticism: "God is a spiritual sphere (or circle), whose center is everywhere and whose periphery is nowhere." ["As formulated in the *Poimandres* of Hermes Trismegistus; cf. Mahnke 1966, p. 44"] (p. 143)

The image of a world soul gradually devolved into an image of the individual's soul within to be discovered by self-knowledge and sacrifice of ego desires. Medieval mystics like Meister Eckhart believed the individual human being carries a "divine spark" or likeness of God in the deepest hidden center of his or her psyche where God lives and acts. Most mystics thought of this center as pure spirit which excluded the natural creature and matter. (von Franz 1975, p. 144) The *cosmic* mandala image, the mathematical geometrical symbol of God and the cosmos, became a favorite god-image of the first natural scientists and the great mathematicians and philosophers like Nikolas von Kues, Pascal, and Leibniz. For them the image was cosmic *and* personal. (p. 144, 150)

The essential characteristic of the mandala is that it points to orientation in chaos; to order and meaning. (von Franz 1975, p. 150) Von Franz sees the mandala as womb or matrix of the "psychic ground" being more feminine than our common cultural representation of a more personal God. Feminine mandala symbols include Buddha's lotus and the golden city, Eden divided into four parts, the temenos, the fortress, the round vessel (p. 145) and Jung's Bollingen round tower as a mandala in stone. (p. 146) Von Franz associated the first comprehensive emergence of a god-image "more closely related to maternal nature and to the mother-image of matter" with the beginnings of natural science in the West. (p. 145)

Renaissance culture turned away from the medieval, masculine, spiritual god-image and "turned toward the earth and the principle of matter." Poimandres' writings in the rediscovered *Corpus Hermeticum* helped restore the mandala as a model of the godhead and the cosmos. It affected the thought of Marsilio Ficino and Giordano Bruno, with Bruno seeing the Ptolemaic and Copernican world-systems as mandalas with deep religious and magical significance. From Bruno the tradition moved to Robert Fludd and Johannes Kepler. (von Franz 1975, p. 150, 151) Descartes' system of coordinates is also a mandala that von

Franz describes as "a primordial vision which came up from the unconscious." (discussed in von Franz 1986, "The Dream of Descartes," p. 57 ff) Mandala imagery is reflected in Niels Bohr's model of the atom and Walter Boehm's model of the electron as the infinite sphere with its omnipresent center. Von Franz comments, "Apparently, whenever man finally confronts something unknown of basic importance this image is constellated in the outer world as well as in the inner, as a symbol of a final transpersonal *order*." (p. 151)

The mandala now finds a place in modern mathematical theories and biological concepts of the Self and the concept of selves within selves. (see volume 1, Appendix D: Self and Organism) The later was illustrated by Jung's Liverpool dream. (MDR, p. 197-199) Quantum mechanics further supports the organism Self concept with the premise that everything is interrelated and influences everything else. Complexity theory describes the self-organizing abilities of psyche *and* matter and points to a possible underlying order in what appears to be chaos or in what can emerge out of chaos. Subjectively the processes are experienced as a centering, implying a center in the psyche, and symbolically portrayed as such.

Jung discovered the mandala in the depths of his unconscious and in his analysands. He associated it with the process of realizing the Self—the "real personality," the "complete man," the Anthropos, the "god within." (von Franz 1975, p. 151) "In mandalas drawn by modern men and women," von Franz notes, "it is often a star, a flower, a cross with arms of equal length, a precious stone or a human figure, etc., but almost never a god image." (p. 152) Noble-prize winning nuclear physicist Wolfgang Pauli dreamt of a world clock formed of two intersecting circles that gave him "an impression of most sublime harmony." (CW 12, ¶ 308) The place of the deity in modern men and women seems to be taken by an image of the wholeness of man (CW 11, ¶ 139) or replaced by an inner psychic center with the image of a "great all-embracing human being (Anthropos) or...a mandala." (von Franz 1975, p. 154)

Jung chronicled the evolution of the god image:

> The gods at first lived in superhuman power and beauty, on the top of snow-clad mountains or in the darkness of caves, woods, and seas. Later on they drew together into one god, and then that god became man. But in our day even the God-man seems to have descended from his throne and to be dissolving himself in the common man. (CW 11, ¶ 141)

The mandala has the essential function of creating inner cohesiveness but this sense gets robbed if projected onto a group. (von Franz 1975, p. 152, 153) If the personal is not differentiated from the archetypal (Jung's No. 1 and No. 2 personalities), the individual ego is prone to inflation by identifying with the god-like powers that have unconsciously invaded us. Inflation at the collective level leads to becoming victim to "the hypertrophy and totalitarian demands of the idealized State." (p. 152)

APPENDIX C

The Anthropos

Jung associated the collective unconscious or collective psyche with the archetype of the Anthropos, the Cosmic Man. The Anthropos was believed to be the source of all that is created, it fills the universe, and is found within. It is the basis of feeling at one with the environment. (von Franz 1975, p. 125) Anthropos and mandala images are produced by the collective unconscious to counter a certain dissociability in the human psyche resulting from the large number of archetypes and instincts. The Anthropos is the psychic element that opposes the boundless drive to live out any single instinct and it doesn't exclude "any essential human disposition, not even inferior and contrasexual elements." It is an image of the bond that unites all humans, "the preconscious ground of all communication and community among men (p. 138)":

> Since the Self in its deeper layers is of a collective nature, it represents and makes possible the *participation mystique* of all human beings, "the unity of many, the *one* man in all men." That is why it becomes visible in the image of a cosmic man...who is one and the same time the innermost being of the single individual and of all humanity. [CW 10, ¶ 419] (p. 258)

Hindu tradition and some Western Gnostics recognize the Cosmic Man as an inner psychic image. Hindus use meditation and yoga to calm the mind and desires so the Cosmic Man can emerge from within. (von Franz 1964, p. 203) Old Hindu myths speak of Purusha, meaning "man" or "person," the only immortal part of man who "lives within the heart of every individual, and yet at the same time he fills the entire cosmos." (p. 202) This is a way of saying we have particularly human and individual ways of experiencing universal forces. The goal is to go beyond the purely physical aspect of existence by recognizing and experiencing the "eternal," archetypal realm, especially the archetype of the Self; to recognize and allow oneself to be led by the inner Great Man.

The Anthropos in a form of the Self frequently appears in origin myths as a gigantic man who pervades the whole cosmos. It represent the *prima materia* from which everything else arose "and the basic substance of all later human generation," or the condensation of all human souls into a timeless, transpersonal unity:

> The *Edda*, for example, describes how the gods shape the world from the body of the original giant Ymir. (von Franz 1975, p. 122)

> There is a Jewish legend that when God created Adam, he first gathered red, black, white, and yellow dust from the four corners of the world, and thus Adam "reached from one end of the world to the other. According to another Jewish tradition the whole of mankind is contained in Adam from the beginning, which meant the soul of every-body who would ever be born. (von Franz 1964, p. 200)

The Cosmic Man has been identified with Christ, Krishna, Buddha, the Old Testament "Son of Man" and in later Jewish mysticism as Adam Kadmon. (von Franz 1964, p. 202) Christ is a kind of collective soul, "the one 'inner Christ' within the multitude." (von Franz 1975, p. 122, 123) The Gnostics gradually broadened the phallic god Hermes into an Anthropos figure in late antiquity, "a cosmic image of a god man who animates all of nature" (p. 25), making the Anthropos the basis of feeling at one with the environment. (p. 125) This divine spirit symbol-izes the "union of spiritually alive and physically dead matter" and personified the secret the alchemists and Hermetic philosophers sought in nature. (p. 26)

In late antiquity the Gnostics had a dramatic myth of a "Light Man" or the Antrhopos as the personified principle of light "who is identical with the supreme godhead." Evil star powers persuaded him out of a spiritual beyond and he fell or flowed down into matter and broke into thousands of sparks of light or became scattered throughout matter as a "crucified world-soul." He waits for redemption through a Redeemer sent by God *or* the effort of the single individual to free the pneumatic original being within himself and to return with him to the kingdom of light. This gnostic Anthropos lived on, underground, in the alchemical tradition and in Hermetic philosophy, down to the beginning of the contemporary period. Similar elements are also to be found in Jewish images of the Messiah.

In [a] lengthy text of the gnostic sect of Ophites...the phallus, "which strives from the lower to the upper things," is an image for the Anthropos, sunk in matter and longing to return to the world of light. He is buried like a corpse in matter, awaiting his resurrection, which comes about through the efforts of the single individual in the interest of the development of his "inner man." (von Franz 1975, p. 123)

The Ophite story locates the genesis of the movement towards enlightenment within the most basic drive in living organisms—the sex drive. In human males, symbolically and archetypically relating to the phallus can become the first step on a journey towards wholeness by experiencing what Jung called the dark, chthonic side of God.

Because Christ as an Anthropos figure uniting humanity lacked darkness and bodily and material reality, it failed to liberate "the true man." The alchemists in the Middle Ages began to project a different Anthropos image into *matter*. Being the natural scientists of their day they strove not for their own redemption but to liberate God from the darkness of matter as did their Gnostic predecessors. "The divine Anthropos they sought to free from matter was an image of man in which good and evil, spirit and matter, were genuinely united and through which not only man but also all of nature would be made whole." (von Franz 1975, p. 135, 136) The Romantics brought the visionary power of the arts to bear upon the sensations of the body and from nature to create, in William Blake's case, a Resurrected Body of Christ, an Anthropos figure. (see Appendix A)

The god-man image is constellated and alive in contemporary man as singular projections of Nietzche's Superman, Marx's "true man" and Teilhard de Chardin's new Christ image (similar to Matthew Fox's concept of Christ in *The Coming of the Cosmic Christ*, 1988). As von Franz notes, "At the bottom it is the image of man in the Aquarian Age which is being formed in the collective unconscious." In the constellation Aquarius, the water bearer is the Anthropos as a Self-image who pours water from a jug into the mouth of the Southern Fish representing something still unconscious. (von Franz 1975, p. 136) Jung described the jug as "the vessel of consciousness" and the pouring action is the directing of conscious energy towards the unconscious. (p. 284) Von Franz suggests, "This could mean the task in the Aquarian Age is to become conscious of the larger inner presence, the Anthropos, and give utmost care to the unconscious *and to nature* instead of exploiting it." (emphasis added, p. 136)

APPENDIX D

Merlin and the Grail Legend

Writer Laurens van der Post believed the medieval myth of the Quest for the Holy Grail is the most important myth for our time—if we could live it. In an interview with Nancy Ryley in *The Forsaken Garden* (1998, p. 15-52), van der Post explains how the story transformed the Middle Ages through the discovery of the feminine and the spiritual quest for wholeness. (p. 41) Through popular sagas, Merlin, the great magician, medicine man and bard of Celtic mythology, got joined as early as the Middle Ages to the evolving Christian mythos of the Grail, a feminine vessel.

Van der Post challenges us in our own contemporary way to be as bold and adventurous as the knights of old and go on a journey of imagination and spirit in search of our wholeness. Wholeness and holy are derived from the same word: "To make whole was to heal, was to be whole, because in the beginning all sickness was spiritual sickness... even more, almost, than a sickness of the body." (Ryley 1998, p. 41)

Van der Post believed the Grail Legend was the greatest in the English-speaking world because the Grail is a container. "*Grail* is an old Provencal word for a great vessel which was put on the table at night and the whole family, the whole community, would partake—eat—out of the common bowl." It symbolizes a container of spirit, compassion, and love that we can all partake of. (Ryley 1998, p. 42) Ryley describes its significance for an individual, a culture, and our relationship with nature:

> The Quest for the Grail carries within its imagery the search for the mystical *center* known to all cultures since our earliest beginnings...Our greatest task is to consciously re-create ourselves through that journey to the center where each

person's uniqueness lies. Early tribal peoples spoke of the hub of the universe as the place where everything was created, and believed that whenever we are in tune with the harmonies of Creation we become that center. (p. 47)

In her chapter, "Le Cri de Merlin," Marie-Louise von Franz in *C. G. Jung: His Myth in Our Time* (1975), notes that many legends and works of poetry revolved around the vessel of the Holy Grail and the Grail stone in the Middle Ages and up through the 17th century. It was part of a Gestalt of a period of knighthood, chivalry and alchemical symbolism that anticipated the problems of the new age. Wolfram von Eschenbach's epic poem *Parzival* replaced the Grail vessel by a stone that had fallen from heaven, "the *lapis exilis*, the term used by the alchemists for 'their' stone." The Grail was also described as a leaden vessel used by Nicodemus to catch the blood as it flowed from the heart of the crucified Christ. In another version Christ appeared to Joseph of Arimathea in prison and gave him the vessel containing his blood, making Joseph the first Guardian of the Grail. A series of Grail Kings succeeded him. (von Franz 1975, p. 269) Blood was thought of as the seat of the soul and the life principle of any creature. The Grail vessel, compared with Christ's tomb in some texts, would then contain "the living soul of Christ," von Franz explains, "the mysterious essence of his being" that continues to work in the world to "give forth the healing effect of his presence." (von Franz 1975, p. 269, 270)

Similar motifs are seen in the Egyptian Osiris myth. The Pharaoh incarnated the sun god Ra during his lifetime, and became the god Osiris in death. "[Osiris] represented the passive, dark, feminine side of the godhead and of nature," writes von Franz. He was murdered by the demonic god Seth who shut him in a lead coffin and threw it into the sea. The coffin washed ashore and hung suspended from a heath bush. In some versions of the Grail legend the lead Grail vessel containing Christ's blood fell into the sea and washed up in France where it hung from a fig tree, only to be discovered when it began to work miracles. (von Franz 1975, p. 270)

Alchemists identified Osiris' lead coffin with their alchemical retort as early as the third century of this era, describing it as the real "secret of alchemy." The Isis mysteries of late antiquity represented Osiris by "a round vessel filled with water from the river Nile...' a symbol of the sublime and ineffable mysteries of the Goddess.'" A snake was often engraved or carved on the handle. "This snake is the numen who guards the tomb and protects the transformations of the god," notes von Franz. "Psychologically it symbolizes the deepest levels of the collective unconscious, where the transformation of the god-image occurs." (von Franz 1975, 270) She offers a psychological interpretation of "this mythological motif of the god who continues to live after his death in a vessel filled with a living substance (blood, water from the Nile)": when the reigning god-image ages and dies, its elements sink back into the origin of such images, the hidden background of the unconscious psyche. (p. 270, 271)

Dreams and visions kept alive and bore witness to Christ's reality in early Christianity, but symbol formation in individuals got repressed with the institutionalization of belief. Christianity rigidified,

> but the living continuity of psychic life preserved that which was lost to collective consciousness. Both poets and common people began to weave fantasies around the idea of the tomb of Christ (one thinks at once of the Crusades) and the vessel which contained the living psychic mystery of Christ. (von Franz 1975, p. 271)

The vessel is a *feminine* symbol, "a maternal womb in which the figure of the god-man is transformed and reborn in a new form," also a gnostic motif and part of the Osiris myth. Gnostics believed a god higher than the ambiguous world-creator sent down to humankind a mixing vessel (krater) for immersion of those who sought spiritual transformation and a higher consciousness. (von Franz 1975, p. 271) Zosimos of Panopolis, one of the most important of the early alchemists, absorbed this gnostic teaching and subsequent alchemists continued to work with the motif of the mysterious vessel of transformation. The vessel was seen as being identical with its contents, including fire, water, Mercurius and the stone. In medieval mysticism it became an image of the soul which receives divine grace and reveals the future and the hidden through the voice of an invisible presence. (p. 271, 272)

The Grail legend includes the motif of the "old sick king"—Amfortas suffering from a thigh, or genital, area wound that does not heal. Amfortas is the fisher king and the Christian era is associated with the Age of Pisces, its symbol being two fish pointed in opposite directions. Jung and von Franz associated this king with an aging or senescent Christianity with its unresolved sexuality issues, currently playing out as child sexual abuse in the Catholic Church. Amfortas could not recover and hand over his authority until the pure, innocent Parsifal asked him about the Grail. Parsifal sees the Grail but does not ask the question, then goes on a journey where he encounters several dark Anthropos figures (Appendix C) that he is unable to come to grips with. Failure to form a union with the dark brother delays the performance of his task. (von Franz 1975, p. 274)

Jung associated the spiritual suffering of his father with Amfortas: "I as a 'dumb' Parsifal was the witness of this sickness during the years of my boyhood, and, like Parsifal, speech failed me." (MDR, p. 215) Years later he realized the issue had been taken up by the gnostics in the earliest days of Christianity, and later by the alchemists who sought the panacea to Amfortas' wound. The male figure that emerged out of Jung's unconscious subsequent to Elijah and Solome was Philemon, the Egypto-Greek figure with a Gnostic flavor and the wings of a kingfisher (fisher king). Philemon was a winged spirit, or meaning, whose earthly counterpart was a spirit of nature, a Mercurius-type figure associated with Jung's phallic self-image. (p. 184, 185; Appendix H: Jung's Phallic Self-image)

In studying a culture, one looks for complimentary and compensatory motifs to the dominant religion in the legends, stories, and folktales of that culture. In several French versions of the Grail saga, Parsifal, in his search for the Grail, "keeps coming across the tracks of a mysterious being who is finally revealed as the real 'secret of the Grail.'" This figure is Merlin, who presents himself in several different guises to Parsifal, giving advice or a commission. (von Franz 1975, p. 275)

When Jung said Europeans were far from being modern and hadn't finished with the Middle Ages, he was alluding to the issues addressed by the Grail legend and Merlin. In these legends and sagas, the collective unconscious of the European was attempting to integrate Christianity with its "pagan" past including shamanism, a sacred connection with nature, and the sensuous and sexual energies associated with old European goddess cults. (see volume 3, Appendix G: The Sacred Prostitute and the Erotic Feminine and Appendix H: The Black Goddess) At the other end of the spectrum, the Oglala Sioux holy man Black Elk, born in 1863, underwent a tremendous struggle to integrate his background with the Christian message. (see DeMaille 1984, *The Sixth Grandfather*)

A medieval legend describes an envious Satan who wanted to be incarnated as a human being so the *dark* God could become human. Merlin was begat by the Devil who as an incubus impregnated a pious virgin without her knowledge: the shadow story to the Annunciation to the Virgin Mary. (von Franz 1975, p. 162, 163). Merlin's pious mother and his teacher, the priest Blaise, influenced him to renounce the evil inclinations inherited from the Devil. The primal opposites in Christianity of the unresolvable conflict between Jesus and the Devil exist together in Merlin's character despite him becoming a seer and bringer of health and wholeness. (p. 275)

Merlin could see into all people and foretell the future. Stonehenge was erected on his advice, and after conveying the story of the Grail to the King, he called upon the King to set up the table of the Grail in relation to the first Grail table of the Last Supper. The King set up the requested Round Table in Carduel, Wales, of strong Celtic roots, and gathered fifty of the best knights. Merlin announced he would be far away from then on and he didn't want the knights to know he brought about the Round Table. (von Franz 1975, p. 275, 276) This is typical of the unconscious to produce powerful healing images and processes before receding again into the background.

Merlin was later associated with the birth and coronation of King Arthur before once more returning to the forest, having gone mad with suffering over the war between the Britons and the Scots. A house was built for him in the forest, his *esplumoir* or place for transformation, where he devoted himself to astronomical observations and singing about future happenings. He appeared as "a hairy wild man or a friend and guardian of forest animals." A spring miraculously broke out near his tower that cured a madman and cured Merlin from his despair over the warring among men. (von Franz 1975, p. 276, 277)

His laugh was famous and his knowledge of the future made him lonely because he knew so much more than others. When very old, he taught many pupils about things of the spirit before he "with[drew] into eternal silence," vanishing into his *esplumoir* or into a rock tomb. On occasion heroes would meet over his stone before setting out on a brave adventure. (von Franz 1975, p. 277) Other versions of the saga had him in love or become bewitched by a fairy—Viviane, Niniane, la Dame du Lac (Lady of the Lake) or Morgane (probably the Celtic water goddess Muirgen). (p. 285) In the Viviane story Merlin falls in love and disappears with her into the beyond, "and now only his distant cry is heard, the famous 'cri de Merlin.'" (p. 277, 278)

Merlin is an archetypal figure of the ilk of shamans, medicine men, pagan hermits and Christian forest friars. Both Elijah of the Old Testament and John the Baptist in the wilderness are pictured as being unusually hairy hermits, a characteristic associated with Merlin. Elijah appears in the legends of late antiquity and the Middle Ages identified with the Metatron, God's first angel, who was called "the little Yahweh." The Metatron was also equated in late antiquity with Enoch and John the Baptist. Von Franz describes this as an image for the individuation process, as seen from the unconscious side, that "amount[s] to a process of incarnation of the godhead" in the form of a man. (von Franz 1975, p. 278)

The hairiness of Merlin leads to a close association with stag symbolism, related to the Celtic god Kerunnus and alchemical Mercurius as *cervus fugitivus*—the fugitive stag. Since Mercurius best personifies the alchemical transformation substance, Merlin himself is therefore the secret of the Grail vessel. (von Franz 1975, p. 278, 279) Jung understood his Grail dream from his 1938 visit to India to mean, "Seek the Self within, and then you will find both the secret of the Grail and the answer to the spiritual problem of our cultural tradition." (p. 279)

Jung was shaken when he became acquainted with the details of the Merlin saga almost 20 years after his Grail dream. (von Franz 1975, p. 279) Without being aware of those details, he had done and experienced much of what Merlin represented—Jung's stone tower retreat at Bollingen and the spring later discovered there, the Elijah visions, and Jung's primal laugh that Laurens van der Post described as a laugh "like the first man on earth." Jung wanted to chisel "le Cri de Merlin" into the cubic stone in his Bollingen courtyard that represented the essence of Bollingen. (p. 279, 280)

Legend had it that the poet and bard Taliesin later joined Merlin in his forest observatory. Beautiful shamanic poetry ascribed to Taliesin describes an individual who can shift his shape like a god and become the sea, wind, sun, rocks and all the elements of nature. Mercurius was also a shape-changing god and a spirit pervading all of nature. (von Franz 1975, p. 281, 282) Jung occasionally had similar experiences at Bollingen. (MDR, p. 225, 226)

Like Merlin, Jung looked into the future and sought its signs in the artistic expressions of the collective unconscious. Jung searched for what was new and psychologically creative amongst the disintegration portrayed in the arts. (von Franz 1975, p. 282) He noted the mandala symbols of totality in the paintings of Erhard Jacoby and Peter Birkhauser. (CW 10, ¶¶ 724 ff) Von Franz wrote an excellent commentary on many of Birkhauser's powerful paintings presented in *A Light in the Darkness: The Paintings of Peter Birkhauser*. (Birkhauser 1980)

In certain sagas where Merlin disappears after being bewitched by a fairy, he gets entangled with her in a hawthorn patch or lowered into a grave containing two embalmed lovers—an alchemical image of the partners in *coniunctio* in the retort. Heinrich Zimmer said of Merlin's withdrawal, "The unconscious, having given a hint of the mystery to the world, sinks back into stillness." Merlin consciously yielding to Niniane's enchantment brings consciousness to the timeless realm of the collective unconscious—a journey of shamans, magicians and Indian yogis. From this timeless position Merlin hovers over time and looks into the future. (Zimmer 1939, p. 15 f, 154 in von Franz 1975, p. 285)

As Jung drew near the end of his life, he became preoccupied with his near death images of a "sacred marriage" he had almost twenty years earlier:

> Merlin's disappearance into the union of love with Niniane suggests [a] death-and-marriage motif. At the same time he becomes again what he was from the beginning, a "spirit in the stone." He is *entombe*, or *enserre* in a stone grave, and from there his voice can be heard. From time to time certain heroes meet at this stone before setting out upon great adventures. This stone grave is at the same time also a nuptial couch and the vessel of the *unio mystica* with the godhead. (von Franz 1975, p. 286, 287)

APPENDIX E

The Philosopher's Stone

Marie-Louise von Franz in *C. G. Jung: His Myth in Our Time* describes the philosopher's stone as one of many alchemical images of the Self, of god in man. It is created by the alchemical processes of active imagination and reflection that seeks to embody the spirit in matter and in nature.

Beginning with the earliest alchemical texts, the philosopher's stone was equivalent to the gold sought by the alchemists. The "stone sent by God" was God's mystery in matter which had a spirit (*pneuma*) hidden in the stone or in the human body which had to be extracted. This stone was the starting point and the goal of the alchemist's opus and it could turn any metal into gold. It corresponds to the diamond body of Chinese alchemy that the alchemist creates through meditative exercises in order to attain immortality during his lifetime (Richard Wilhelm, *The Secret of the Golden Flower*). (von Franz 1975, p. 220)

In Jungian terms, once one has experienced and consolidated a personal sense of the Self after transmuting the hardships in life (the lead), one can re-enter the body and the world with a transforming perspective (everything is turned to gold). The re-entry becomes the spirit embodied, spirit with a corporeal sense to it.

Several Western alchemists suspected the opus was not literally turning lead into gold but was a meditative development of their inner personality that would then complete itself in the outer world. The "stone" was a kind of immortal body for both Eastern and Western alchemists. In an early Egyptian burial ritual, a stone column called the *djed* pillar was erected in the grave to represent the moment of resurrection. (von Franz 1975, p. 220, 221) "One of the oldest Greek alchemical texts," von Franz writes, "celebrates the production of a stone...as a resurrection mystery in which a 'statue' comes forth from the fire reborn." (p. 221)

The *lapis* (stone) in Arabian alchemy was equated with the Ka'aba in Mecca, and when alchemy re-entered the West the authors found a parallel between "their" stone and Christ as "the stone that the builders rejected [which] has become the cornerstone." (Matthew 21:42 RSV) Some alchemists identified the alchemical stone with Mercurius and mercurial water, even with a subtle spiritual and corporeal stone as a resurrecting body that could penetrate and pervade anything. (von Franz 1975, p. 221) This secret stone comes as a gift from God, grasped only by the spirit through inspiration or divine revelation, which fixes and makes the soul permanent. Alchemical associations link the last Judgment with the germination and birth of the stone, in which the soul is beatified and united with the original body, to eternal glory. (CW 12, ¶ 462) The Aztec's put a precious stone in the mouth of the dead to revive them after death and the Egyptians tended and worshiped stone statues of the gods "because they were expected to preserve the imperishability of the Pharaoh's life-principle (Ka)." (von Franz 1975, p. 221, 222)

Jung thought the alchemists stone as a god image was a perfect complement to the official Christ image that he felt was too spiritual, rarefied and remote from the human heart. The stone emphasizes the principle of matter, is found everywhere, and is "cheap": "Its fabrication lies within the reach of every man." (CW 13, ¶ 127) In it the "flesh" is glorified because the spirit appears to be condensed or fixed in matter. (von Franz 1975, p. 231)

The stone symbolizes the inner god in man as a "son of the universe" (*filius macrocosmi*) and not the "son of man" like Christ because it did not come from the conscious mind but "from those border regions of the psyche that opens out into the mystery of cosmic matter." (CW 13, ¶ 127) The philosopher's stone is man's redeemer, like Christ, *and* a god who must be redeemed by man. (CW 12, ¶ 557) The alchemist was unconsciously working on redeeming God, not man, and failed to recognize himself as the equivalent of Christ as a symbol of the Self. (CW 12, ¶ 452) This is self-evident to the Indian mind and von Franz believes it accounts for the attraction of the West to the Indian spirit. Alchemy prepared a bridge to bring the unconscious contents into consciousness (von Franz 1975, p. 232, 233) and was a symbolic process that could bring about an inner transformation.

The Gnostics had a similar deep understanding of Christ as a symbol of the Self, but they were inflated by believing the mystery they possessed made them superior to the "formless multitude." They identified with their own light and confused the ego with the Self, forgetting that enlightenment only has meaning when it helps one to recognize one's own darkness and see that dark and light are equals to be united into a third "'free from the opposites,' beyond all moral categories." (CW 11, ¶ 438) Von Franz asks:

> Are we today, after two thousand years, mature enough to understand and realize man's divinity without forgetting our smallness and darkness? The phenomenon of the Self, in which all the opposites are united, is...simply inconceivable, a mystery with which one had better not identify, as long as one is in possession of one's normal faculties. Man himself cannot master the uncanny polarity within his own nature; instead he must learn to understand it as an objective psychic content within himself, as a numinous experience which in the past was reserved for the few, but which takes hold of more and more people in the contemporary world. The stone *is* an experience within us, but it is not the ego. (von Franz 1975, p. 233)

APPENDIX F

Jung and Mithraism

Jung experienced transformative encounters with his anima when engaged in active imaginations in 1913 during the early phases of his "confrontation with the unconscious." Through these imaginations he felt he had been initiated into the Mithraic mysteries which, as Richard Noll (1992) points out, incorporated a malevolent view of the feminine. That view exemplifies Jung's difficulties with Eros and sexuality and eventually it was through Parsifal that he found a healing image.

In lectures given in 1925 Jung commented on his first descent into the unconscious where he met Elijah and Salome. He spoke of his inner development for the first time with comments of a tone not conveyed in *Memories, Dreams, Reflections*: "As I am an introverted intellectual my anima contains feeling [that is] quite blind. In my case the anima contains not only Salome, but some of the serpent, which is sensation as well." Salome seemed "evil" to him: "When Elijah told me he was always with Salome, I thought it was almost blasphemous for him to say this. I had the feeling of diving into an atmosphere that was cruel and full of blood." (Jung 1989, p. 93 quoted in Noll 1992, p. 22)

Not mentioned in *MDR* is Jung's remarkable account of a second descent into the unconscious in December, 1913 a few nights after the first descent. He began by seeing the white and dark sides of a sharp-edged mountain ridge and a fight between a white and a black snake associated with their respective sides of the ridge. Jung considered both snakes to be "dark principles." After the black snake was defeated and its head turned white, Jung saw Elijah mount a Druidic altar mound. It shrunk in size along with Salome, a snake and a house as walls grew around them that created a descent into the underworld (Jung 1989, p. 96 in Noll 1992, p. 22, 23):

> Then a most disagreeable thing happened. Salome became very interested in me, and she assumed I could cure her blindness. She began to worship me. I said, "Why do you worship me?" She replied, "You are Christ." In spite of my objections she maintained this. I said, "This is madness," and became filled with skeptical resistance. Then I saw the snake approach me. She came close and began to encircle me and press me in her coils. The coils reached up to my heart. I realized as I struggled, that I had assumed the attitude of the Crucifixion. In the agony and the struggle, I sweated so profusely that the water flowed down on all sides of me. Then Salome rose, and she could see. While the snake was pressing me, I felt that my face had taken on the face of an animal of prey, a lion or tiger. (p. 23)

Jung associated Salome's approach and worship with his inferior function "which is surrounded by an aura of evil. I felt her insulations as a most evil spell," he said. (Jung 1989, p. 97 quoted in Noll 1992, p. 23) He believed he had experienced the "mystery of deification" (Noll 1992, p. 12) resulting from Salome's performance (Jung 1989, p. 98 referenced in Noll 1992, p. 24) that "gave certainty of immortality," (Noel 1992, p. 12) claiming that the imagination was "Mithraic symbolism from beginning to end." (Jung 1989, p. 99 quoted in Noll 1992, p. 24) In his lectures and writings Jung had made many references to the ancient mysteries of classical Greece and Rome (Noll 1992, p. 14, 25) and was aware that initiations in most of these cultures, including Mithraean, occurred in subterranean locations (cf. the cave in the childhood nightmare and in his "house-of-many-levels" dream). (p. 16) "The animal face which I felt mine transformed into was the famous [Deus] *Leontocephalus* of the Mithraic mysteries," Jung said. "[Statues have] only been found in the mystery grottoes (the underchurches...)... chosen as symbolical of a descent into the underworld." (Jung 1989, p. 98 quoted in Noll 1992, p. 24) Richard Noll (1992) explores Jung's lion-headed transformation in his provocative article, "Jung the *Leontocephalus.*"

Jung identified the *Leontocephalus* as "Aion, the eternal being" in Hellenistic mythology, describing Aion based on the scholarship of his time:

> He is represented with the winged body of a man and the head of a lion, and he is encoiled by a snake which rises up over his head...He is Infinite Time and Long Duration; he is the supreme god of the Mithraic hierarchy and creates

and destroys all things...He is a sun-god. Leo is the zodiacal sign where the sun dwells in summer, while the snake symbolizes the winter or wet time. So Aion, the lion-headed god with the snake round his body, again represents the union of opposites, light and dark, male and female, creation and destruction. The god is represented as having his arms crossed and holding a key in each hand. He is the spiritual father of St. Peter, for he, too, holds the keys. The keys which Aion is holding are the keys to the past and future.

...Some of [the ancient mystery cult psychopompic] deities are equipped with the keys to the underworld, because as the guardians of the door they watch over the descent of the initiates into the darkness and are the leaders into the mysteries. (CW 18, ¶ 266, 267)

Jung told his audience, "It is almost certain that the symbolical rite of deification played a part in these mysteries." (quoted in Noll 1992, p. 24) The Self as Aion is depicted in the frontispiece in CW 9, ll, a volume entitled *Aion: Researches into the Phenomenology of the Self.* On the right thigh is a crab, the sign of Cancer that begins with the Summer Solstice and on the left thigh is the goat, the sign of Capricorn that begins with the winter solstice. Jung said, "The lion is the young, hot, dry July sun in culmination of light, the summer. The serpent is humidity, darkness, the earth, winter." Noll comments, "He interprets the image of a Mithraic amphora with a flame arising from it that depicts a lion on one side and a snake on the other as 'opposites of the world trying to come together with the reconciling symbol between them.'" (Jung 1989, p. 98 quoted in Noll 1992, p. 24) Jung closes his lecture by saying, "In this deification mystery you make yourself into the vessel, and are a vessel of creation in which the opposites reconcile." (Jung 1989, p. 99 quoted in Noll 1992, p. 24)

Jung's understanding of Mithraism came largely from Franz Cumont's Christianized presentation:

Mithras was an ancient Iranian solar god (like Helios) and a god of correct behavior and order (like Apollo). He is referred to in inscriptions as *Sol Invictus*, the "invincible sun." Mithraism was a survival of the old dualist Mazdaen religion of ancient Persia, but adapted to the world of the Roman empire. (Noll 1992, p. 26, 27)

Only men participated in the mysteries that spread throughout the empire from the 1st to 4th centuries CE. Cumont described their initiation ceremonies as being very similar to the Roman Catholic mass but with the holiest moment being the unveiling of "the ubiquitous image of Mithras killing a bull, the tauroctony." (p. 26, 27) In actuality, there is no account of the central myth or of the ceremonies. (p. 27, 28, 54 notes 45, 47)

Jung put Elijah, Mithras, al-Khadir (Muslim), Christ and Mercurius into the same archetypal pantheon of Anthropos figures. (CW 18, ¶ 1529) He was captivated by the central icon of tauroctony where he interpreted Mithras as the "sacrificer and the sacrificed," but "it is only his animal nature that Mithras sacrifices, his instinctuality." (CW 5, ¶ 668) In 1910, Jung had rejected Freud's interpretation of the bull-slaying as "the killing of the animal ego by the human ego, as the *mythological projection of repression*, in which the sublimated part of the human being (the conscious ego) sacrifices (regretfully) its vigorous drives." (McGuire 1974, 199a F) Instead of "an unconscious censor that keeps the instincts out of awareness," Jung put forth "a more pagan interpretation that views the Mithraic bull as an accepted alter-ego of Mithras." (Noll 1992, p. 32) Jung said the accepted fecundity symbol of the bull "is slain by another sexual symbol. The self-sacrifice is voluntary and involuntary at once (the same conflict as in the death of Christ)." (McGuire 1974, 200 J quoted in Noll 1992, p. 32) When Jung wrestled for two months writing his chapter on "The Sacrifice" in *Symbols of Transformation* (CW 5) it was over this very issue. (p. 31) It is, as Noll puts it, "The triumph of Jung's broader concept of the libido over the strictly instinctual (sexual or venereal) libido theory of Freud." (Noll 1992, p. 32) Jung knew this interpretation would sacrifice Freud and his relationship with Freud, whom he knew was in the astrological sign of Taurus. (p. 32, 33)

Recent scholarship suggests the bull sacrifice may relate to the discovery in 128 BCE of the procession of the equinoxes. This led to the hypothesis of "the existence of a new divinity responsible for this new cosmic phenomenon, a divinity capable of moving the structure of the entire cosmos and thus a divinity of great power." (Ulansey 1989, p. 93 quoted in Noll 1992, p. 31) "Mithras was this deity, and he is seen killing the bull because it symbolizes the ending of the cosmic age—the Age of Taurus—just prior to the age in which Mithraism was born [the age of Pisces]." (Noll 1992, p. 31)

Noll makes a convincing case that Jung felt he was initiated specifically into one of the seven grades of Mithraic initiation known as *leo*, the lowest level of full participation and membership in the mysteries. (Noll 1992, p. 33, 34) *Leo* was Jung's astrological sign and it is ruled by Zeus. Lions were associated with the sun, fire, purity, mediation between gods and men, and the constellation Leo. (Noll 1992, p. 35)

Noll observes that the lion-headed figure into which Jung was transformed lacked wings and the clutched keys of the classical Aion figure, but these aspects and other Mithraic qualities were incorporated by the Philemon figure that first appeared in a dream at some point in December 1913. "Philemon is an Aion figure that combines Mithraic and Gnostic elements," Noll notes. (Noll 1992, p. 38) With Philemon as Jung's new *imago dei*, new Self-image, Jung moved "from a fascination with one ancient tradition (the Mithraic mysteries, circa 1910-1914) to another (Gnosticism circa 1916)." (p. 38, 39)

Noll also associates the negative elements of Salome's character with Mithraism. He assumes the rites of passage through the seven stages of initiation necessitated separation from women. The status of *Pater* ("father") as the final stage is of course masculine. The hero-myth important to Jung at this period of his life and the basis of *Symbols of Transformation* concerns "the triumph over the urge to regress or return to the mother." Achieving *pater* status "would be equivalent to the successful outcome of the challenges of the hero, the triumph of the whole personality over the 'infantile personality' that wishes to regress." (p. 39, 40)

Within the Mithraic cult, women were associated with hyenas, animals with "a peculiarly malevolent, corrupting and polluting aspect to them. They are associated with 'human witches or sorceresses,' indeed the *lamia* of ancient Greek folklore" and the only animal with the evil eye. (Noll 1992, p. 40, 41) Hyenas were held in high regard by magicians for their power to "snare men whom [they have] driven out of their minds" (Gordon 1980, p. 60 quoted in Noll 1992, p. 41) and could magically paralyze by looking at someone. Women were also believed to "possess the evil eye, the power to bewitch and fascinate men" and derange them. (Noll 1992, p. 41) Echoes of a Mithraic perspective on women appear in Jung's seminal *Seven Sermons to the Dead*. (MDR, p. 388, 389)

Salome did not have the evil eye in Jung's vision as she was blind— a blindness healed by Jung's Christ-like crucifixion that turned him into what Jung interpreted to be an Aion Self-figure. An alternative, non-Mithraic interpretation of Jung's vision is Salome seeing in Jung

Christ-as-Eros—"God is love"; a dimension of Christianity Jung could not easily relate to. The snake is associated with the deep unconscious and with Jung's sensation function. To be gripped by the snake as part of the Gestalt with blind Salome would be to sense and embody the deep feeling states. Rather than the masculine Mithraic associations with the lion that Noll developed, one could begin with the lion as the archetypal ultimate association of the cat with the feminine. For Jung to become the Christ of love/Eros, he would have to have the strength and courage, the heart of a lion, to endure the struggle with his deeply wounded Eros side. This would feel like a crucifixion when the snake reached the heart level, leading to another identity with Christ, and would raise his Eros/feeling side to consciousness, healing Salome's blindness.

The theme of the union of opposites, logos and eros, male and female, by a *mysterium coniunctionis* was to occupy Jung for the rest of his life. Heart attacks and heart problems plagued Jung in his old age as he continued to wrestle with the mysterious union. His attempt to put his personal confrontation with the unconscious between 1913-1917 into a historical and cultural context evolved from Mithraism to Gnosticism to alchemy by the late 1920's, where the feminine is of equal importance to the masculine. Jung's relationships and his wrestling with his body-based emotional side is detailed in Appendix G: Jung's Eros Wound and His Image of God while his self-identification with the phallus and its relationship with the feminine as unconscious matrix is presented in Appendix H: Jung's Phallic Self-image.

Jung was fascinated by the Greek Magical Papyri of the 2nd century BCE to the 5th century CE and his practice of active imagination and descent into the unconscious bears a relationship to the magical procedures they present (Noll 1992, p. 46, 47 note 11):

> The ancients believed that, in practice, "self-knowledge can be obtained by some kind of consultation of the 'personal daimon'" (Betz 1981, p. 160) rather than through the outcome of philosophical self-examination...

> "...For them...'consult your personal daimon' implies that the Delphic maxim orders them to conjure up their personal daimon and get control of it by magical procedures; when that daimon appears, the magician can then submit questions and receive answers. This type of interpretation and procedure is what we find in [the Greek Magical Papyri]." (Betz 1981, p. 160 quoted in Noll 1992, p. 47 note 11)

Hillman described Jung's psychological method: "Know Thyself in Jung's manner means to become familiar with, to open oneself to and listen to, that is, to know and discern, daimons." (Hillman 1983, p. 55 quoted in Noll 1992, p. 47 note 11) Noll observes, "Such experiences seem to be uniquely human and are universally reported, regardless of cultural complexity or epoch." (p. 47 note 11) Freud may have practiced another magical procedure whereby statues were animated "for the purposes of divination and self-knowledge." Anecdotal evidence is that Freud engaged in imaginary dialogues with statuettes to inspire him and help focus and develop his thoughts. (p. 47, 48 note 11)

John Haule (1992) discerns an important evolution in Jung's concept of the hero as it relates to Western attitudes towards the feminine and sexuality. It is seen in the difference between the hero myth in Jung's *Symbols of Transformation* that has a more Mithraic caste and its evolution into Parsifal as hero described in Jung's *Psychological Types* (CW 6), his first publication (1921) after his confrontation with the unconscious. When writing *Symbols* Jung thought of the hero as one

> who has to stand up to a devouring Great Mother figure threatening to drag him back into symbiotic unconsciousness. His entry into her womb/tomb and successful re-emergence constitutes his own renewal and transformation. The temptation to incest, therefore, is no longer—as with Freud—a literal or symbolic genital seduction played out with the personal mother. In Jung's mythic view, it is a seduction to blissful dissolution in the collective unconscious, the generating matrix of conscious life. (Haule 1992, p. 99)

The hero executes a daring entry into the Terrible Mother (the unconscious) and is "transformed as they fight their way free." (p. 107)

Jung argues that sexuality did not cause Amfortas' fall in the *Parsifal* legend but rather it was the fault of the cultural perspective on sexuality, aggression, and power that inhibits a proper relationship to these powerful energies, causing them to remain brutish, anima-instinctual like, compulsive, and seductive. (CW 5, ¶ 371-373) Parsifal as the pure fool becomes Jung's new model of the hero by surviving the crucifixion of seeing, feeling, and reflection on both sides of the archetypal split in the Western psyche. The hero's only hope is that the transcendent function, that works irrationally, will spontaneously "produce an image that bridges the gap." (Haule 1992, p. 106)

Eroticism and sexuality are an inimical part of the gestalt of deep journeys into the unconscious. Sex is at "the crossover point where spirit and body flow into one another" (Haule 1992, p. 106), a "sexual longing for an ecstatic union of spirit and body," Haule writes. (p. 108) It is only through empathy and compassion for ourselves and others and all aspects of our archetypal drama that we are able to feel, reflect and understand—and move on with the aid of integrating symbols. Haule calls this the "business of 'gaining wisdom through empathy'" (p. 109) from a refrain in *Parsifal*, "knowing through empathy, the pure fool." (p. 112 note 15)

APPENDIX G

Jung's Eros Wound and His Image of God

Looking at Jung's life through the lens of attachment theory reveals a deep Eros wound in Jung's psyche. It is for this reason that British psychoanalyst Donald Winnicott said every analyst should read the first three chapters of *Memories, Dreams, Reflections.* The wound not only affected Jung in the realm of intimacies and relationships but more profoundly in his concept and experience of God. It made it particularly difficult for Jung to relate to the central figure in Christianity, Christ himself.

The root of Jung's insecure attachment is in his disturbed connection with his depressed, hysterical, ghost-fearing mother whom Jung felt had abandoned him when hospitalized during his infancy. By April 1958 Jung had finished writing the section in his autobiography about his early years having made a supreme effort to be objective in understanding and presenting the powerful emotional nature of his childhood. (MDR, p. vi, viii) Yet in the John Freeman interview for BBC in March 1959, Jung said he didn't have the slightest idea why he as a child was afraid of his mother at night. (Jung 1977, p. 427) Winnicott diagnosed Jung as a schizophrenic after reading the first two chapters of his autobiography (Winnicott 1964) but one must realize the schizophrenic label was more readily dispensed in the 1960s when Winnicott wrote. Winnicott and Hillman noted that when one is abandoned, the phallic sexual can be overwhelming (cf. Jung's phallic nightmare as a child). Von Franz associated the phallus in Jung's childhood dream with Eros and a deep connection with his analysands, but many people, including Emma Jung, noted "that the ideas a patient brought to Jung were far more interesting than the actual person." (Bair 2003, p. 262. Also see p. 736 note 41 and p. 823 note 41)

Jung had problems similar to Freud in his basic nature and in his manner of relating to people. (note 59) His analysis of Freud's neurosis may have an element of projection of himself when he surmised that Freud's delicate sensitivity probably indicated his emotional life had been "severely disturbed." (Bair 2003, p. 722 note 50) Michael Fordham, a British Jungian analyst who integrated object relations theory into Jungian psychology, said "Jung was a narcissistic personality and had a lot of paranoia to deal with. Such people are never satisfied"; they never feel fully recognized or appreciated. (p. 818 note 24)

Jung's deep abandonment and intimacy complex would have been strongly activated by the split with Freud. Jung had looked up to Freud as a respected father figure. He was a father who knew much about Jung's unconscious through analysis of Jung's dreams, Emma's analysis with Freud, and Sabina Spielrein going into analysis with Freud after her intimate relationship and analysis with Jung. Freud was cruel and attacked Jung on a deeply personal level after the breakup, certainly a big factor in the depth of despair Jung experienced as he began his descent into the deep levels of the unconscious between 1911-1913.

Jung associated women with personal relations and "the function of Eros," saying it is their "tremendous cultural task...to unite what Logos has sundered." (CW 10, ¶ 275) Jung interpreted his two near death experiences and a subsequent heart attack in 1946 as not being right with his attitude and to his wrestling with the infinitely incomprehensible problem of the *hieros gamos*—the *mysterium concunctionis*. (Hannah 1991, p. 294, 295) The *concunctionis*, the union of opposites, would include the union of Logos and Eros. Jung looked at illnesses from a psychological perspective and heart problems following the heart attack included tachycardia, an erratic and racing pulse; a "disease" of the vegetative or autonomic nervous system. The heart has strong symbolic associations with love and Eros. Could his deep problem with Eros have been the main factor behind "an improper attitude in life" that lead to the heart attacks? He clearly had a powerfully developed logos, with understanding and a search for meaning being his life-long quest.

An overriding impression from his 1944 near death experience was a "strange cessation of human warmth." Not once did he think of anyone on earth or have any regret of leaving them. He looked forward to being with people in the afterlife who would give him the archetypal context of his life and his place in history—not a vision or experience of divine love or a reunion with dead friends and relatives.

Toni Wolff was Jung's soulmate during his confrontation with the unconscious, with Jung saying he probably could not have done it without her, yet von Franz was proud to say, "intellectually, I replaced Toni Wolff in Jung's life,"and gained Jung's confidence because, as she saw it, Wolff "was too much a slightly conventional Christian, and she refused to follow him" in his interest in alchemy. (Bair 2003, p. 371) Jung said of his response to Toni's refusal: "All of a sudden Toni Wolff went out of my life just as fast as she came in. All of a sudden, that was the end." (p. 390) He later explained, "The daimon of creativity has ruthlessly had its way with me." (MDR, p. 358) He was close to some people "so long as they were related to my inner world...[and] appeared within the magic circle of psychology; next moment, when the spotlight cast its beam elsewhere, there was nothing to be seen... And I myself am the victim; I *cannot* stay." (p. 357)

A powerful Self-image for Jung was presented in a dream that immediately preceded his work on the *conjunctio* in the mid- to late- 1940s. In the dream, the "highest presence," the ultimate image to be worshipped, was behind a door leading to the solitary chamber of Uriah. Uriah was King David's general "whom David had shamefully betrayed for the sake of his wife Bathsheba, by commanding his soldiers to abandon Uriah in the face of his enemy." Jung saw Uriah as a guiltless victim who prefigured Christ, "the god-man who was abandoned by God," as was Job. (MDR, p. 219) Note that the compassionate, loving, forgiving side of Jesus was not emphasized as the ultimate in Jung's Self-image. One of Jung's most emotional writings, *Answer to Job*, concerning the Biblical Job story, may have gripped Jung because it was a story of ultimate betrayal (by God). Jung said God atoned for his torture of Job and God became human when he identified with Jesus feeling totally abandoned on the cross. (CW 11, ¶ 647)

I propose that Jung's Eros wound led him to emphasize the dark side of God that he saw as necessary to compensate a too-light Christianity. I feel that because of his Eros wound Jung was unable to adequately convey the vital role of love and intimacy essential for becoming a whole human being. Because of his wounds Jung could not relate to the essence of Christianity's message—God is love. Jung's God was primarily associated with Personality No. 2, a dazzling realm of *nature devoid of humans*—a world of divine beauty and stark cruelty. His best description of God was "the name by which I designate all things which cross my willful path violently and recklessly, all things which upset my subjective views, plans and intentions and change the course of my life for better or worse." (Jung 1961b) This has echoes of the intrusive, fearful phallus of his childhood nightmare that jolted Jung's psyche into premature consciousness. It led to a split from the body and in many ways from people and reality. Winnicott associated Jung's vision of God shitting on the beautiful Basel Cathedral with Jung's own destruction of beauty. At its most primitive level, Winnicott saw "[Jung's] destruction of the good object because of its being real in the sense of being outside the area of his omnipotence." His depressed mother made it difficult for Jung to get at his primitive aggression; a primitive destructiveness that he remained in fear of throughout his life. (Winnicott 1964, p. 454) It came forth in an archetypal manner in his description of the dark side of God in *Answer to Job*.

I contrast Jung's near death experience with that of John Robinson, a former anthropology professor at the University of Wisconsin, Madison who was clinically dead for 45 minutes following a massive heart attack. Part of Robinson's experience included sitting with a divine being who radiated love. In the presence of that being Robinson examined his life, feeling tremendous sorrow for many of the things he had done to others. That to me is the true "last judgment," a self-judgment arising only after feeling contained by divine transcendent love.

A relevant cultural experience occurred on the last night of Jung's 1920 visit to North Africa: he had a disturbing dream of wrestling with a dark Arab prince who tried to drown him. Jung associated the prince with Eros and emotions, a prince he saw as the dark side of God, the dark side of the Self. He perceived the Muslim desert culture of North Africa at that time to be a childlike, primitive culture. (see volume 1, Appendix B: The Animal Soul, The Primordial Mind, and Archetypes)

Jung experienced the frightening depths and extremes of the psyche to the extent of the dark side of God and the collective dimension of Evil in Christianity. Winnicott associated this with Jung being a schizophrenic, albeit a schizophrenic who healed himself. (Winnicott 1964, p. 450) The fact that Jung developed the means to work his way through this dark realm and use the experience to heal himself and others puts Jung solidly in the archetype of the wounded healer. Factors associating Jung with the shamanic tradition of a wounded healer are his sense of ghosts and spirits, his respect for parapsychololgical phenomena, and his emphasis on the necessity of recognizing and relating to "the two million-year-old man within." Every tribe depended on the shaman to negotiate the mythic realm in order to keep the tribe in alignment with it and to see into the future. That was Jung, particularly in his identification with the Celtic shaman Merlin.

Jung's descent into the unconscious between 1911-1917 bears several resemblances to a shamanic journey. *The Seven Sermons*, a product of that journey, are an outpouring of deep unconscious material that laid the foundation for his path to individuation and the rest of his life's work. His descriptions of Eros and the feminine in the *Sermons* are of Biblical dimensions. The ultimate for the individual as described in the *Seven Sermons* was distinctiveness and singleness, associated with being superior to others and avoiding slavery. Ultimate value is associated with effective thought and depicted as a white bird; a half-celestial man *"chaste and solitary,"* (emphasis added) flying above the earth and abiding with the celestial mother, a manifestation of the god of heaven and spirit. "He bringeth knowledge from the distant ones who went before and are perfected" and bears our words to the mother, "a vessel of the sun," who intercedes and warms but has no power against the gods. (MDR, p. 388) (Two prominent anima figures in Jung's life—Maria Moltzer and Toni Wolff—had ascetic, nun-like qualities. See note 40 and Bair 2003, p. 192, 559) In *Sermons*, communion with others is associated with submission to others and is opposed to the valued singleness. It is only to be engaged in to the extent necessary when we often feel weak over against the gods. (MDR, p. 386-388)

Phallos/sexuality is described in *Sermons* as a superhuman daemon which is a manifestation of the god of the earth. It is an earthy soul presenting itself as a serpent who has the nature of a woman—"a whore… wantoneth with the devil and with evil spirits; a mischievous tyrant and tormentor, ever seducing to evilest company." Crafty thoughts creep in through her and she pricks us with intemperate desires. She seeks the company of the dead who are held by the earth—"they who found not the way beyond that leadeth to singleness." However, the she-serpent is useful to us because she is beyond our grasp, "thus showing us the way." (MDR, p. 386-389) Note the strong association of evil with the earth, the feminine, seduction, and sexuality.

Richard Noll describes how Jung's experience of Salome in his initial descent visions in 1913 reflect "many of the Hellenistic attitudes towards both women and hyenas" as being "malevolent magic/the evil eye/the power to destroy the minds of men." (Noll 1992, p. 41) (see Appendix F: Jung and Mithraism) Jung associated Salome with his inferior function, feeling, "which is surrounded with an aura of evil. (Jung 1989, p. 97 quoted in Noll 1992, p. 23) His reaction to Elijah telling him he had always been with Salome, his blind feeling side, made Jung feel he was "diving into an atmosphere that was cruel and full of blood." (Jung 1989, p. 93 quoted in Noll 1992, p. 22)

In *Answer to Job*, Jung emphasized that the cruel, unrelated side of God was due to an absence of the feminine in the Jewish religious tradition. The sacred feminine began to appear in the form of God's partner Sophia about the time the book of *Job* was written. The Jewish ban on eating pork, the pig being a prime symbol of the Great Goddess, and the destruction of the Golden Calf by Moses can be associated with a repression of a type of worship of the feminine associated with Mother Goddess cults of the Near East. The archetype of the Sacred Prostitute and the erotic feminine of the Near Eastern cults were huge problems for Jung as mentioned in his comments in *Sermons*. (see volume 3, Appendix H: The Black Goddess and Appendix G: The Sacred Prostitute and the Erotic Feminine) Jung bemoaned the absence of the feminine in the Christian Trinity, and was elated with the 1951 papal declaration of the bodily assumption of Mary into heaven, seeing this as a very positive evolution in Christian belief.

An image of the feminine in its archetypal mothering and nurturing form was problematic for Jung as revealed by a disturbing dream during his student days. In response to a wish for a direct experience and sighting of God, he dreamt of a big sow atop a huge pile of manure. (Bair 2003, p. 397, 660 note 45) The association of waste and feces with the nourishing Great Mother as a Goddess image was understandably disturbing to Jung.

One must remember Jung wrote the *Seven Sermons* and experienced North Africa before his transformative work with alchemy and the *hieros gamos*. Jung had to live with the difficulty and embarrassment of having two wives in a very restrictive and uptight society because it was the only way he could go through the depths of the psyche. Jung probably experienced a full sense of wholeness after he suffered through the Eros losses of Toni Wolff and his wife Emma. He added the last addition to Bollingen after their deaths, saying it expressed his true self after it emerged from under the spiritual and maternal realms the two women represented for him. (MDR, p. 225)

Winnicott saw Jung's lifelong quest for wholeness as an attempt to experience the childhood need to have parents living as a *conjunctio* (Winnicott 1964, p. 451) and to experience a well grounded "unit self" capable of engaging the many problems of the world. (p. 455) He saw the mandala as a defense against coming to terms with "destructive-ness, and with chaos, disintegration, and the other madnesses." (p. 454, 455)

Winnicott's analysis of Jung can be put into an archetypal framework and returned to Jung's system made possible by the system's broad, flexible, and inclusive structure. Namely, the lacuna in Jung's work can be redressed by incorporating the archetype of the Great Mother as a foundational and sustaining love.

APPENDIX H

Jung's Phallic Self-Image

Daniel Noel's article, "Veiled Kabir: C. G. Jung's Phallic Self-Image," (1974) follows a thread of phallicism throughout Jung's life beginning with his childhood nightmare of an underground phallus. More particularly, it is veiled, secret, and hidden phallic energy. Jung's nightmare was a gestalt of a hidden (under the earth) phallus associated with light and "a certain type of clothing—especially an unusual hat of some kind and a long frock coat or cloak, perceived as a *disguise*." (Noel 1974, p. 226) This was the clothing of the male mourners at Jung's father's funerals and the dress "disguise" of the fearful Jesuit priest. (MDR, p. 9-11, 13) The gestalt also included "the somber image of burials; in particular a black coffin-box and an underground stone chamber." (Noel 1974, p. 226)

Jung associated the manikin he carved at age ten with Telesphoros—the "boy genius of healing" accompanying Asklepios, Greek god of healing ("Aesculapius," 1959, p. 262, 263 quoted in Noel 1974, p. 228); "a dwarf-like, nocturnal figure, a child in a hooded cloak" (Kerenyi 1959, p. 56-58 quoted in Noel 1974, p. 228) concealing its bright nature. (Kerenyi 1959, p. 119 note 24 referenced in Noel 1974, p. 229) Telesphoros was a helper of Asklepios and known as the "sender of true dreams," "the boy who fulfilled dreams," "life-bearing" or "light-bearing," and "life generating." (Meier 1967, p. 38, 39 quoted in Noel 1974, p. 238) His relationship to Hermes was revealed by a statuette of Telesphoros with a removable top concealing a phallus and inscribed "boundary neighbor." (Meier 1967, p. 38 referenced in Noel 1974, p. 238) Kerenyi saw an identity between Telesphoros and "the *Genius Cucullatus*, or hooded spirit, 'a figure found in many parts of the Roman empire.'" (Kerenyi 1959, p. 119 note 23 quoted in Noel 1974, p. 229)

At age forty-five Jung did a stone carving of a phallic figure and named it the "'breath of life,' the creative impulse," and associated it with the manikin, its soul stone, and the phallic nightmare. Jung said, "the manikin was a *kabir*, wrapped in his little cloak, hidden in the *kista* [prehistoric European coffins found in earthen burial mounds], and provided with a supply of life-force, the oblong black stone." (MDR, p. 23) Kabir refers to the "Cabeiri," Phrygian underworld fertility gods known as the "mighty ones" or "great gods." A major Greek initiation cult worshipped a father-son pair of *cabeiri* as "the power of fertility, symbolized by the male organ of generation." ("Cabeiri" 1959, p. 497 quoted in Noel 1974, p. 230) They were depicted as pygmies with prominent penes. (Kerenyi 1955, p. 56 fig. 2 referenced in Noel 1974, p. 230)

When Jung traveled in India in 1938, he described himself as being a "homunculus in a retort," using this phrase in association with his truth. (MDR, p. 274, 275) The homunculus is a little man the alchemists produced in their retorts (like a kista) and can be related to Telesphoros and the Cabiri. (Noel 1974, p. 232) When hospitalized in Calcutta Jung dreamed of rescuing the Grail, a dream that included "a tiny, iron, hooded gnome, a *cucullatus*," scurrying about the side of the Grail castle. (MDR, p. 281)

Jung described his Bolllingen Tower as "a maternal womb" where he could be "reborn in stone" and achieve wholeness. (MDR, p. 225) He said he lived his "true life" at Bollingen as the "age-old son of the mother." (p. 234) As he carved a rejected stone that became the symbol of Bollingen, he saw a sort of eye in the stone that looked at him so he carved an eye into the stone and put "a tiny homunculus" in its center. "This corresponds to the 'little doll' (*pupilla*)—yourself," he said, "which you see in the pupil of another's eye: a kind of Kabir, or the Telesphoros of Asklepios." (p. 227) Jung chiseled a line into the stone that linked Telesphoros with Mithras, a divine savior of Persian origin, who was born from a rock and associated with the sun, portrayed as "a youth with a conical cap and flying drapery, slaying the sacred bull." ("Mithras," p. 622-624 quoted in Noel 1974, p. 235) This is Telesphorus as a redeemer, or savior figure for Jung, "that like the sun he blazes up out of the darkness" and is associated with phallic virility—the bull. (p. 235) (see Appendix F: Jung and Mithraism) Another line Jung carved referred to Kyllenian Hermes' golden staff, the *caduceus*, originally two snakes coiled around a cypress branch. The *caduceus* was a symbol of healing and Asklepios's symbol. Barren women hoped "to be impregnated in their incubation sleep by Asklepios in the form of a snake," a phallic form that Asklepios often appeared in. (Kerenyi 1959 p. 32-36, 39-41 referenced in Noel 1974, p. 237)

Jung's final construction at Bollingen, completed five years before his death, extended what he described as being himself—"the small central section which crouched so low, so hidden." (MDR, p. 225) With Bollingen as Jung's "symbol of psychic wholeness," Noel sees this addition as "a final moment of externalization or bringing-into-consciousness, a kind of epiphany, of the shining phallic core...[that] gripped him most deeply and personally." "The 'primal form' of C. G. Jung," says Noel, "is the hermetic phallus." More particularly, it is a phallus "veiled" or "disguised" in a hooded spirit form, "or kista, in alchemical retort or underground chamber—ultimately in the tomb/womb of mystery and unconsciousness." (Noel 1974, p. 239) Jung described his sense of being in his last addition to Bollingen [which he thought of as Merlin's retreat (Bair 2003, p. 758 note 64)] as being in "a sort of grave," a grave in which he had many creative ideas. (Noel 1974, p. 324)

Noel remarks, "Jung's orientation to this psychic energy was necessarily masculine...The creative power thrusting up out of the eternally uncreated, the birth of light and breath of new life" was clearly phallic for Jung, but "never entirely unveiled. That is, we can see the phallic self-image of C. G. Jung as *essentially* 'hermetic,' as a secret, undisclosed apart from its maternal or feminine containment." (Noel 1974, p. 239, 240) This sense is related to Jung's main concepts of the unconscious and God, as wanting and not wanting to become conscious and of his psychology being connected with "the age-old story of the newly risen divine light" that brings release and redemption from the primordial darkness and maternal mystery of the unconscious. (MDR, p. 274)

Kerenyi observed that the secret Cabirian cult "was the creation of primeval woman in the stork goddess, whose maternal care was devoted to budding life, to the scion, the sun rising in the human body." (Kerenyi 1955, p. 58 quoted in Noel 1974, p. 240) Noel adroitly linked this with Jung's African experience of seeing the sun rising out of the darkness—the "maternal mystery, this primordial darkness." The natives considered the *moment* the sun rises to be sacred, not the sun itself, a moment bringing "redemption, release." (MDR, p. 269) "The Mithraic aspect of the kabir—the phallus-as-solar—would be so only in the very instant of its blazing epiphany, when it is still dependent, so to speak, upon the care of the darkness. We could also surmise," Noel writes, "that as a hidden or hermetic phallus, Jung's Hermes is already virtually hermaphroditic." (Noel 1974, p. 240) The Kabeiroi were associated with "the wider group of distinctly male deities (Kuretes, Korybantes, Idaioi, Daktyloi), who made up the retinue of the Great Mother" (Kerenyi 1955, p. 48 quoted in Noel 1974, p. 241 note 13) and appeared as "ghostlike phallic demons," "now Titanic, now dwarflike or spiritlike." (p. 49 quoted in Noel 1974, 241 note 13) "Kerenyi describes the 'Kabirian primeval man' as 'a spirit still in process of birth'" (p. 56) and suggests that the meaning of the Kabirian mysteries is that "'the dwarflike and earthy, the wild and crude male principle...is elevated into higher spheres by a winged femininity.'" (p. 57 quoted in Noel 1974, p. 241 note 13)

This "primeval man" would be the deep somatic level of the unconscious where Hermes is close to "the two million-year-old man within" and the animal soul, where synchronicities are more likely to occur. (see volume 1, Appendix B: The Animal Soul, the Primordial Mind, and Archetypes) Jung's phallic self-image cannot be dissociated from his life-long focus on the deep levels of the psyche and his association of "fantasy as imaginative activity" with "the direct expression of psychic life." He described imagination as being "the *reproductive* or creative activity of the mind in general." (emphasis added, CW 6, ¶ 722)

APPENDIX I

The Conscious Feminine

Jung stated that one of our greatest needs in the West was for a recognition and incorporation of the archetypal feminine into science and culture. Jungian analyst Marion Woodman provides one of the more comprehensive statements on the nature and means of doing this in an interview with Nancy Ryley in *The Forsaken Garden* (1998).

Woodman maintains that for the first time we have "to perceive the sacredness of matter in order to survive." (Ryley 1998, p. 117) She believes the evolution within the psyche is pushing towards recognition of the conscious feminine—"an awareness of our subtle body in our material body." (p. 94) The subtle body is developed by getting in touch with our bodies and the body generated images that arise. Without sacred images of gods and goddesses addictions arise as the spiritual gets projected into the material realm. (p. 62, 64) Concrete *Mater* (Latin for mother) is worshipped instead of a feminine deity. (p. 65) Spirit gets concretized into matter by such means as food addictions (the concretization of the nourishing archetypal feminine), alcoholism (the concretization of the "spirits"), and drug addictions (the concretization of the transcendent).

Woodman sees the repressed feminine as the archetypal shadow of our culture in the form of its patriarchal/negative mother complex. (Ryley 1998, p. 76) The wounded masculine in the patriarchy gets expressed as an aggressive, competitive thrusting towards a goal. (p. 65, 66) Archetypal positive masculine in the male and female is assertive energy, discretion, discernment, and clarity—"clarity that moves toward a goal." (p. 66) The feminine principle, as Woodman sees it, is "process, presence, being here now, paradox, resonating, receiving, surrendering, listening." (p. 72) It is connected with feeling, of knowing what is of value to oneself—"a gut response in the body." (p. 71) The positive feminine is grounded in a nature where all matter is sacred—the realm of the goddess. The negative mother is associated with a concretization of matter, a dense unconscious matter disconnected from instinct and spirit. (p. 77) Power and control then step forth to attain possessions and when a threat to our material possessions is felt. (p. 65)

Several *disciplines* help develop a sense of the sacred: Jungian psychology, meditation, working with imagery (any creative work), and working every day on self-discipline. Like a good athlete, one must practice, be disciplined and listen to one's body so as not to "drive it beyond its capacity." "Freedom is living your essence to its absolute fullness. And you can't do that without discipline—daily, hourly discipline," Woodman writes, physical, emotional, and spiritual discipline. The human body is a miracle, and to experience it you have "to eat proper food, exercise, and listen to the messages it conveys." (Ryley 1998, p. 84) When we are in touch with our bodies we "know when to stop eating, or drinking, or consuming." (p. 107) Purify, simplify, discipline, "A discipline of love," as Woodman describes it. (p.102)

Psyche wants to be whole and the soul causes trouble in mind and body if it is not whole. The wisdom of the body must be brought to consciousness to be transformative and for one to achieve wholeness. This is done by listening to the body, inhabit the body—Feldenkrais, Tai Chi, Yoga, etc., aid the process. (Ryley 1998, p. 86) "Soul matures through our senses" and it loves to play. "Play has to do with the imagination and with the whole excitement of creativity, and with the constant re-creating of oneself through inner images." (p. 81) The soul moves the body and is life itself: "The body that is truly expressing soul is a healthy body. And it loves to move, and life is movement," writes Woodman. (p. 87) One must find a process that connects one to the body unconscious, and then reflect on what emerges. (p. 89)

Woodman sees passion, chaos, and illness as three important areas to handle properly. Of crucial importance is to keep the passion alive in one's life. "Many people have to remain unconscious in order to keep their job, so they don't let the passion out," Woodman observes. (Ryley 1998, p. 85) The work rhythms are often too fast and exacting. (p. 80) Rage builds up in a repressed soul, settles in the musculature, and suppresses the immune system. (p. 88, 89) "Chaos turns our value systems upside down." (p. 96) It crucifies us between different value systems. Crucifixion is, "in part, taking responsibility for your own life and staying with the pain and the conflict until you find out who you are." (p. 97) You have to forgive yourself for being human with all the lust, rage, grief, and jealousy we all have within. (p. 92) Illness can be a big part of life and it has a way of "put[ting] many things in place." One has to let go and accept the reality of the illness and the body: either you get turned around or you die early. (p. 103) To deal with these things we must surrender to the unknown, learn patience, and trust the Dream Maker for a solution. Illness, loss of a loved one, simply is. You become bitter if you ask in suffering, "why me?" (p. 99)

The essence of the process, as Woodman describes it, is the soul as the Goddess surrenders to the penetration of God, the spirit. The manifestation of God in matter is the Goddess according to Woodman. Experiencing the energy and creativity of that Divine Embrace in one's body is the soul as "embodied essence," part spirit and part matter. (Ryley 1998, p. 94) Because metaphor connects the eternal and the temporal worlds, "the soul lives on metaphor." (p. 86) "Soul work is incarnation" where the eternal, archetypal realm of image and metaphor is allowed to play in the body and release the energy of the image by focusing on the images and experiencing them in the body. (p. 86, 87) A meandering, playful, sensual, creative and imaginal attitude is necessary. (p. 81) Woodman emphasizes the importance of expressing the metaphors in life and dreams through poetry, music, and other forms so we can see and realize the embodied soul in space/time. (p. 86) (see Appendix A: William Blake and the English Romantics)

"Conscious feminine" is being fully in touch with the body physically and in a metaphoric sense. "That 'embodied essence' is the container strong enough to take the penetration of light, of spirit." (Ryley 1998, p. 94) A guiding concept is to see the body as "the temple in which your soul lives, which one day the holy spirit might visit, then you treat it with awe." (p. 84) Woodman sees the feminine principle as being grounded "in all living nature" with nature and matter being sacred. (p. 76, 77) It loves to "be" and is the opposite of the "two-dimensional, logical, goal-oriented, perfectionist, either-or world" that lacks real life energy. (p. 77)

Being in tune with Divine Will is *kairos*: "You are where the universe wants you to be at any given moment." (Ryley 1998, p. 104) "You as an individual are in harmony with the wishes of universe. There's a moment when everything lines up and you can feel it lining up, and you know 'this is it.'" It's a spiral and not a chronological line associated with the patriarchal pattern. (p. 104) "You and the other energy are one" as you are both in *and* out of yourself. The spark of God or

Goddess within is in tune with the God and Goddess of the universe. (p. 105)

Dreams are an important part of the process. They are "connectors between body and soul" and "pictures of our spiritual connection." (Ryley 1998, p. 86) The dream is part of the metaphorical body that arises from the body and one needs body-generated images to act with confidence in the world. (p. 93) Dreams facilitate the painful soul-making process that leads to maturity through cutting away the false and illusory in one's life. (p. 95) Sacrificing the old can be painful:

> The psyche isn't out to destroy us; the psyche is essentially very kind. It will test us to the very limit of letting death take away the old—symbolically or literally. But then it will bring new life in on the other side. That process is very well-balanced by the psyche. And the dreams guide us in that process. (p. 96)

Nature helps us reconnect with our souls through its beauty of multiplicity of forms, colors, rhythms, and movements. "Soul recognizes itself in that beauty and order," says Woodman. (Ryley 1998, p. 96) We also see nature's cruel side and accept its rhythms of death and rebirth. "A fundamental principle of the feminine is that it's a transformation based on death as part of life...[Sophia's] cycle is life, death, and rebirth. Accepting that principle makes death possible." Everyone has to undergo some sort of near death experience and in their own way come to value their Garden. (p. 119)

One has to have a very strong container to surrender, to trust oneself to the Unknown. (Ryley 1998, p. 101) When caught in a painful, insoluble conflict and there is no way out, one can only "surrender to that unknown, that mystery that is greater than oneself. Then something new happens." (Ryley 1998, p. 98) "You burn the heart empty of the ego desires so that the heart is open to become an instrument for the love that transcends it." (p. 99) Sometimes it takes a blow from God to overcome belief in personal strength and to break down rigidity and release unlived life. This brings surrender and the capacity to love. (p. 101) Suffering breaks our hearts and opens then to love from another. (p.111) "Soul surrenders to a Higher Power in order to receive the energy that can magnify the Divine." (p.101) As Woodman describes it, "My conscious feminine container surrenders to the creative masculine. Then life is intercourse with the Divine. Out of that union comes the

Divine Child, the new consciousness." There would be no life, science, art, or culture without imagination. (p. 117)

Surrender is the paradox of becoming totally yourself when you and the Other are one. The ecopsychological link is Marion's belief that you can't violate the earth once you experience this oneness. The oneness is more like "you are danced" rather than "you are dancing." It is a way of life, bit by bit, and costs us everything. "With soul surrender you find purpose, illumination, transcendence." (Ryley 1998, p.105)

If people are too culturally secure they don't want to know what is in the unconscious. That is dangerous as we project the unconscious into TV and movies and onto others. (Ryley 1998, p. 113) The images we "eat" change the body. We have to use the masculine sword of discretion to select good images and eliminate negative ones, (p. 114) and be discerning about relationships, possessions, and use of our time. (p. 115)

Some people by nature or destiny are called to do this painful, soul-reaching work. No one chooses it, yet no one escapes it either. Some would rather die than do it, but Jung said "what is not brought to consciousness comes to us as fate." (Ryley 1998, p. 115) Greater than childhood innocence is the wisdom realized from the price paid for consciousness: one has simplicity and higher innocence. (p. 118)

Woodman proclaims our journey is to make real the god and goddess within as we move toward a totally new ethos, a new masculine and feminine. First we must free ourselves from "the old father and his patriarchal laws that protect the old mother and her deadly security, because they cripple us." (Ryley 1998, p. 112) People perish without vision. (p. 113)

REFERENCES

"Aesculapius." 1959. *Encyclopedia Britannica*. Vol. 1. Benton: Chicago. p. 262-263.

Bair, D. 2003. *Jung: A Biography*. Little, Brown and Co.: Boston and New York.

Bedi, A. 2000. *Path to the Soul*. Samuel Weiser: York Beach, Maine.

Betz, H. 1981. "The Delphic Maxim 'know yourself' in the Greek magical papyri." *History of Religions* 21: 156-177.

Birkhauser, P. 1980. *A Light in the Darkness: The Paintings of Peter Birkhauser*. Birkhauser Verlag: Basel, Boston, Stuttgart.

"Caberi." 1959. *Encyclopedia Britannica*. Vol. 4. Benton: Chicago. p. 497.

DeMallie, R. 1984. *The Sixth Grandfather: Black Elk's Teachings Given to John G. Neihardt*. University of Nebraska Press: Lincoln, NB and London.

Epstein, M. 1995. *Thoughts Without a Thinker: Psychotherapy from a Buddhist Perspective*. Basic Books: New York.

Fox, M. 1988. *The Coming of the Cosmic Christ: The Healing of Mother Earth and the Birth of a Global Renaissance*. Harper and Row: San Francisco.

Gordon, R. 1980. "Reality, evocation, and boundary in the mysteries of Mithras." *Journal of Mithraic Studies* 3.

Hannah, B. 1991. *Jung: His Life and Work: A Biographical Memoir*. Shambala: Boston.

Haule, J. 1992. "Jung's 'Amfortas wound': *Psychological Types* revisited." *Spring Journal*: Putnam, CT. p. 95-112.

Hillman, J. 1983. "The Pandaemonium of Images: Jung's Contribution to Know Thyself." In *Healing Fiction*. Spring: Dallas.

———— 1992. *The Thought of the Heart and the Soul of the World*. Spring Publications: Woodstock, Conn.

Jung, C. G. *The Collected Works of C. G. Jung.* 2nd ed. H. Read, M. Fordham, G. Adler and W. McGuire, eds. R.F.C. Hull, trans. Princeton University Press: Princeton, NJ.

——— CW 5. 1956. *Symbols of Transformation.*

——— CW 6. 1971. *Psychological Types.*

——— CW 8. 1969. *The Structure and Dynamics of the Psyche.*

——— CW 10. 1970. *Civilization in Transition.*

——— CW 11. 1969. *Psychology and Religion: West and East.*

——— CW 12. 1968. *Psychology and Alchemy.*

——— CW 13. 1970. *Alchemical Studies.*

——— CW 14. 1970. *Mysterium Coniunctionis.*

——— CW 18. 1976. *The Symbolic Life: Miscellaneous Writings.*

——— 1961a. *Memories, Dreams, Reflections* [MDR]. Aniela Jaffe, ed. Richard and Claire Winston, trans. Random House: New York.

——— 1961b. Interview. *Good Housekeeping* Magazine. December, 1961.

——— 1973. *Letters.* Vol. 1. 1906-1950. Gerhard Adler and Aniela Jaffe, eds. R. F. C. Hull, trans. Princeton University Press: Princeton, NJ.

——— 1976a. *Letters.* Vol. 2. 1951-1961. Gerhard Adler and Aniela Jaffe, eds. R. F. C. Hull, trans. Routledge & Kegan Paul: London.

——— 1976b. *The Visions Seminars.* From the complete notes of Mary Foote, Books One and Two. Spring Publications: Zurich.

——— 1977. *C. G. Jung Speaking: Interviews and Encounters.* William McGuire and R.F.C. Hull, eds. Princeton University Press: Princeton, NJ.

——— 1989. *Analytical Psychology: Notes of the Seminar Given in 1925.* Princeton University Press: Princeton.

Jung, C. and Jaffe, A. *Memories, Dreams, Reflections.* Editorial manuscript. Countway Library of Medicine, Harvard Medical School, Boston.

Kerenyi, C. 1955. "The Mysteries of the Kabieroi" in *The Mysteries: Papers from the Eranos Yearbooks.* J. Campbell, ed. R. Manheim, trans. Pantheon: New York.

——— 1959. *Asklepios: Archetypal Image of the Physician's Existence.* R. Manheim, trans. Pantheon: New York.

Mahnke, D. 1966. *Unendliche Sphare und Allmittelpunkt.* Stuttgart.

McGuire, W. ed. 1974. *The Freud-Jung Letters*. The Hogarth Press and Routledge and Kegan Paul: London.

Meier, C. 1967. *Ancient Incubation and Modern Psychotherapy*. M. Curtis, trans. Northwestern University Press: Evanston.

"Mithras." 1959. *Encyclopedia Britannica*. Vol. 15. Benton: Chicago. p. 622-624.

Naess, A. 1984. "The arrogance of antihumanism?" *Ecophilosophy* 6: 8.

Noel, D. 1974. "Veiled Kabir: C. G. Jung's phallic self-image." *Spring* 1974. p. 224-242.

Noll, R. 1992. "Jung the *Leontocephalus*." *Spring Journal* 53: Putnam, CT. p. 12-60.

Paskauskas, A. ed. 1993. *The Complete Correspondence of Sigmund Freud and Earnest Jones, 1908-1939*. The Belknap Press of Harvard University Press: Cambridge, Mass. and London.

Ryley, N. 1998. *The Forsaken Garden: Four Conversations of the Deep Meaning of Environmental Illness*. Quest Books: Wheaton, IL.

Schroeder, H.W. 1992. "The tree of peace: symbolic and spiritual values of the white pine." In *The Proceedings of the White Pine Symposium*. p. 73-83.

Shamdasani, S. 2003. *Jung and the Making of Modern Psychology: The Dream of a Science*. Cambridge University Press: Cambridge, UK.

———— 2005. *Jung Stripped Bare by his Biographers, Even*. Karnac: London and New York.

Siegel, D. 1999. *The Developing Mind: Toward a Neurobiology of Interpersonal Experience*. Guilford Press: NY.

Stevens, A. 1994 *Jung*. Oxford Univ. Press: Oxford and New York.

Storm, Hyemeyohsts. 1972. *Seven Arrows*. Ballentine Books: NY.

Ulansey, D. 1989. *The Origins of the Mithraic Mysteries: Cosmology and Salvation in the Ancient World*. Oxford University Press: New York.

Von Franz, M.L. 1964. "The Process of Individuation." In Jung, C. 1964. *Man and His Symbols*. Doubleday and Co.: Garden City, NY. p. 158-229.

———— 1975. *C. G. Jung: His Myth in Our Time*. Hodder and Stoughton: London.

———— 1986. The Dream of Descartes. In *Timeless Documents of the Soul*. Evanston, IL.

Wilhelm, R. 1967. *The I Ching or Book of Changes*. Cary Baynes, trans. Princeton University Press: Princeton, NJ.

Wilhelm, R. and Jung, C. 1962. *The Secret of the Golden Flower*. Cary F. Baynes, trans. Harcourt, Brace & World: London and New York.

Winnicott, D. 1949/1975. Mind and its Relation to the Psyche-Soma. In *Through Paediatrics to Psycho-analysis*. Basic Books: New York. p. 243-254.

———— 1964. "Book reviews." *International Journal of Psychoanalysis* 45: 450-455.

Zimmer, H. 1939. *Merlin*. Corona 9, part 2. Oldenburg, Munich and Berlin.

———— 1946/1972 *Myths and Symbols in Indian Art and Civilization*. Joseph Campbell, ed. Bollingen Series VI. Princeton University Press: Princeton, NJ.

Zimmerman, M. 1991. "Deep ecology, ecoactivism, and human evolution." *Re-Vision* 13: 3, p. 122-128.

INDEX

G

Gestalt 20, 92, 142, 156
gnomes 31, 125
Gnostic 23, 30, 37, 47, 105, 125,
        139, 144, 155
Gnosticism 35, 38, 47, 48, 51,
        155, 156
Gnostics 48, 101, 118, 137, 138,
        143, 150
goddess cults 10, 48, 63, 74, 144
Godhead 47
God-image 6, 15, 25, 125, 134,
        143
"God's world" 10, 11, 13, 14
Goethe 13, 16, 49, 59, 60, 120
Golden Calf 164
Gothic 11
Gowers, John 78
Grail 5, 30, 51, 58, 60, 79, 80,
        89, 125, 127, 141, 142, 143,
        144, 145, 146, 167
Great Man 94, 95, 138
Great Mother 47, 157, 164, 165,
        169
Greek Dactyls 31
"green spirit" 52
Grunhutl 89
Gustafson, Fred 119

H

Harding, Mary Ester 118
Harlow, Harry 48
Haule, John R. 157, 158, 175
healer 81, 99, 106, 162
heart attack 80, 83, 160, 162
Hera 81
herm 30
Hermes vii, 46, 59, 60, 66, 71, 88,
        89, 93, 99, 105, 106, 107,
130, 134, 138, 166, 167,
        168, 169
Hermetic philosophy 114, 134,
        139
hieros gamos 83, 90, 160, 164
Hillman, James 34, 63, 130, 157,
        159, 175
Hogenson, George 102
Holy Ghost 119
Holy Spirit 172
Horus 67
house-of-many-levels dream 22,
        23, 27, 103, 152
hypertension 85

I

I Ching vii, 31, 43, 71, 72, 77, 78,
        92, 115, 177
incarnation 105, 146, 172
incest 22, 25, 103, 157
India v, 69, 73, 74, 77, 78, 79, 80,
        115, 125, 126, 146, 167
indigenous cultures 36, 88
individuation 37, 50, 51, 54, 60,
        80, 82, 91, 106, 109, 112,
        121, 146, 163
individuation process 37, 51, 54,
        80, 106, 112, 121, 146
Industrial Revolution 22
insects 11
instincts 1, 97, 104, 137, 154
Isis 142
Islam 74

J

Jacobe, Jolande 84
Jaffe, Aniela 57, 62, 97, 176
Jesuits 3
Jesus 3, 4, 7, 9, 25, 41, 50, 73,